NIGHT OF THE WORLD

BOOK ONE:

WAY OUT WORLD

A Hollerin' Bebop Ghost Story by Oscar Guardiola-Rivera

Inspired by true events and a text of GWF Hegel

Published 2020 by the87press
The 87 Press LTD
87 Stonecot Hill
Sutton
Surrey
SM3 9HJ
www.the87press.com

ISBN: 978-1-8380698-0-3

Design: Stanislava Stoilova [www.sdesign.graphics]

To our daughters, keep rioting.

Contents

Foreword

The *Night of the World* is a beautiful genre-busting, dub poem novella about a young woman warrior who is seeking not only a new social order but a world in which as a young woman she can find herself mirrored in the world around her.

At the heart of her struggle is her relationship with her mother who has not only subjected her but denounced her. How to find yourself when your mother has refused to recognize a young woman as hers? Implicit in this part of the story is how the oppression of women renders them vulnerable out of fear and desperation to embrace those who negate the feminine as human. How does a woman find herself in the story of man when that invisibility becomes her mother's inauthentic 'truth' about the world?

Crucial to the young warrior's struggle is the search for who she really is as a woman and a warrior. *Night of the World* should then be added to the literature of feminism, particularly women of colour feminism. Yes, written by a man who gets it. More broadly, it is an allegory for our time when the bombardment of promises of security lead to the forsaking of freedom and the search for new "species" of humanity to paraphrase Frantz Fanon's telling grade. We sink into a mire of these false promises and then hang on to them for safety. The anguish of losing your mother as she has sunk into that mire is what makes the protagonist's story so deeply moving.

The form of the novella is at the heart of the story. Some of our most urgent needs and hopes cannot be said in prose. The story unfolds through the poetry of the young warrior's search for a soul worthy of that name. This is a novella whose time has come!

Drucilla Cornell

1   Hoodoo Girl

Get up. Do it now. It's not too late to save your mirrorsoul
from her darkness. But you must do it now. Time's running
out.

Hoodoo girl.

You rootworker you.

Put yourself together and run.

Get up and run.

Run like hell.

Hoodoo girl.

If I had told you this story before. Then you wouldn't
be here right now, blood coming out of your eyeballs, half-
conscious on the floor of this dark corridor fighting for dear
life. Trying hard not to close your eyes and give it all up.

Facing the night of the world.

To say I'm sorry won't cut it. The pain in your chest
right now is too unbearable and my apologies won't alleviate
it. Fuck that.

She found you.

The witch found you.

She wants your mirror she wants your soul.

The inquisitor soul collector.

I don't know how but I know it's my fault.

She found you.

She knocked you down, and now sits on top of you
carving your chest with her fingernails.

She wants your mirror she wants your soul.

Mirrorsoul.

Mir-or-soul

Mira-so-l

mira-tu-sol

Her glowing blue eyes peering at you, drilling your

skull. You look back and everything fades away. You look into her eyes and it all goes away. This place, the howling wind, the black cloud of dead souls descending on the sub in which you and your friends tried to escape. Daylight fades away. Life fades away. The void a vanishing point. I know it must now feel like it was all in vain: having made it alive out of the domed council estate, avoiding the riots, catching the train right before the explosions began, dodging the border police at Docklands checkpoint, convincing your dealer friend White Rabbit to show you how deep the hole goes. I know it must now feel like it was all in vain.

If I had told you this story before. But I didn't. I couldn't. If only I had spoken to you as I do now. A disembodied voice in your head. You would've thought you'd gone mad. Like her. That's my excuse. It's a bad one. I know. Kept silent. Tried to reach you through books and stories. Hiding messages in the empty spaces between lines, in epigraphs, titles, tropes, metre and the music of verse and tom-tom rhythms. In fake footnotes. Like a message in a bottle. I'd hoped that in the end you would remember how to read them. I always had faith in you.

But now it's time to tell you this story. If I'm lucky it won't be too late to save your mirror-soul from the coming darkness.

2 Run

It was mid-day back then. There was time back then. The sun had stopped in the middle of the sky. Its light, so bright, blinded our sight. All of us, all the adults engaged in our pig wars, our eye for an eye, our yours is not bigger than mine. Soon we were left in the dark. Some of us peered straight into that flaming sun as if it were a screen, and saw our own wishes projected onto it. No matter we knew it was all fake, a bad play with smoke and mirrors, a poor magician's trick. We wanted to believe. Some of us lost the will to fight. Others grew weary and fearful having seen what lies in its fiery heart. Like me. Fade out. Fade to blank. Blank imagination burned eyes. I wandered blind into the garden of Paradise. Before long I was lost. Walked into the other side of a looking glass.

On the other side, you can't distinguish wrong from right, shadows from light, up from down. You can't tell apart the demons you summon and command from the ones out to steel your dream light. I stopped telling stories and forgot the incantations. I went away, leaving you behind. Like the other grown ups, I too became trapped in my own visions. And remained there, motionless, watching while the whole world burned. The sun frozen in the sky, a watchful eye looking upon us from up high.

As we got lost, the darkness waiting on the other side grew stronger until those of us who had sworn to protect the light were no longer able to contain it. The darkness peered a hole in the sky, turning the whole world into this replica of life.

It happened slowly. People began to disappear in the very early hours of the morning. A motorcade of unmarked blue Ford Coronas would stop in front of their houses. Men in dark glasses wearing long black coats would take them away, leaving in their stead thoughtless idols and automata, rule-abiding university professors, politicians, and bankers. Some were exiled, others were flown in helicopters and thrown into the ocean. First, the writers, the poets and punk rockers. Guilty of sex thoughtcrimes. Their steampunk deemed unfit for the young. Their books were burned. Their vinyls were broken. The spared few quickly converted. The churches of the End of the World opened their doors and received them in their midst, many becoming preachers themselves or joining the ranks of the black-clad New Inquisitors.

By the time we realised what had happened, it was already too late. We left. I left you behind to join the New New Model Army, to the night that began to cover over the sun now fixated in mid-sky as if some kind of blinding eye or a sign of the end times.

When the human world fell, we went underground.

Here, in the bowels of the earth, we wait.

We wait for you to wake up, to get up and run.

Run.

Run like hell.

Remember all the poems and tales I told you when you were a child? They were warnings against her. Don't look into her eyes. If you do, the night of the world will take you. Don't give up your mirror and your name. Not to her. If she finds out your real name, she will lock it inside a box guarded inside a box hidden inside a box; and with it, your soul. Hold your mirror before her; for she despises her own image.

There's a piece of broken glass to your right. Forget the pain, reach out to it, grab it and stick it into her glowing blue eye with all the might left in your body. She will recoil in pain. Now, get up and run. Run like hell. Don't look back. Keep running.

Run.

Run like hell.

Come to us, run through the night that has now become the inner side of nature, different from its external appearance of lush greenery and shining sun up high reflecting its blinding light in the crystal of tall buildings. For it is only an illusion projected onto a thousand mirrors hidden backstage.

Don't look into the mirrors. The night will take over and turn your mind into a dream theatre. A dark opera all horrorshow and ghostly apparitions, phantoms and monsters and demons out to rob you of your name and your mirror. Your storytelling. Instead, they would leave a shallow mask. An empty husk, the mere echo of our voices morphing into a chorus of cowing crows.

Crow.

Forget about of us. We have become creatures of the night, this empty nothing that contains everything in its silence and simplicity. A wealth of infinite images, none of which belong to us, none altogether present, has erased our appearance and silenced our voices. We tell no stories. Our speech no longer fills the evenings in front of the fire. No songs are sung in funerals. Our tears do not carry the strength of curses, damnations and eutopias.

Not you. You're different. The mourning voice is within you. Your speech comes screaming. Not discourse but a voice in the fire. It unbinds the city.

Later, you may damn the fate that has made of you the righter of wrongs. But not now! Now reach out, grab that piece of broken mirror and poke her glowing blue eye out. Do it. Then get up and run.

Run.

Run like hell.

We will be here waiting.

3　Like Hell

Beware of this world of ghostly imaginations where you exist. For it is night all around it: here a bloody head shoots up, there another white ghastly apparition, suddenly here before it, and just so disappears. You are the only one who can see them but don't stop and don't try to talk to them. Avoid them at all cost, don't confront them. For their magic is powerful. Being air creatures, they can travel through radio waves and speak the language of electronic lines. They're ghosts in the machine gaining their potency from our life of spectacle. Every time we look into our computer screens, they stare back at us spreading through the network as a virus from the future downloaded directly into your very soul, rewriting your mirror and your soul, your inner code and innermost desires.

Yet they cannot enter the page. They abhor the vacuum that is the medium of our images, rhythms and languages, the very fabric of our fables and stories, and cannot understand our attraction for the nothingness that holds two letters or two phrases and two pages together. That is why they seek to control our ability to tell stories and invent languages. This is the reason why they have chosen to forbid all imaging, writing and reading. This is why they plotted to disappear all our writers, destroyed all our libraries, burned all our books, and sought to replace them with the sleek devices that speak directly to your brain in unending beats and blips that leave no empty time for the slowness of thought or contemplation. You know those who use them devices as 'drummers' and 'rococoes'. They're agents from the future. And their masters you know as 'the inquisitors'.

Do not listen to them, take the side roads and alleyways. Avoid them at all cost, and if you can keep your feet in the water, use rivers and canals, set sail and stay in the sea. Whatever you do, don't leave the water. They are less powerful there, in the liquid border that separates your fallen world from the one down underground where we have found refuge. Water stands for the vacuum between one word and the other, between one world and the other, and in water they lose their bearings. Since ancient times we have known that thought, time, and language behave alike, but only now we understand what lies behind this metaphor. As it happens with anything that enters water, the moment you try to capture a thought, buy time, or imprison language, it flows away and vanishes. Truth is the daughter of time.

Think of it as the Merjans and the Scythians used to. For these old people who lived in the border between Finland and Russia, beyond the Achaean peninsula in deep Asia, water is the gateway to eternity and the smoke of the green leaf the key which opens it. They say it is made out of all the lost letters, the half-uttered phrases, the cries shouted out loud against the heavens and all the unfinished stories. Everything that touches water, they say, is there and it is not. Not yet. When the Merjans or the Scythians find a drowned person, instead of burying the body in the ground they put weights on it and commit it once more to the waters of their sacred rivers. That person becomes the object of a tale, an icon or a song. They call telling that tale or singing that song "smoking", as in bringing something out of nothing, as in inhaling the smoke of the green leaf, as in smoke and mirrors. Mirrorsouls. It is their magic it is all the magic. To smoke is to scream, sing a song, tale a tale, or shed a tear, but these screams choke up in one's throat so the words become unintelligible. When a human being screams, say Scythians and Merjans, we declare to all that we want to die, and that it would be very painful not to do so and keep on living. This is love, and it is eternal like time and water.

Hence, to die by drowning is not to die completely according to the Merjans. They say if you drown, your mirror-soul continues its journey through the nulliverse where it joins the ancestors, the loved ones who have departed, and those patiently waiting in the future. It is told in Merjan stories that one's mirror-soul travels through evacuated spaces and voids of different shapes and sizes. The place they call the nulliverse, the void or the interval, is for them jam-packed with nihilists, nihilarians, nihilianists, nihilagents, nothingarians, nullibists, nullifideans, nullunarians, nobodies and nonentities. It's in fact the same for us. These are the nothings our magic invokes, turning them into something. You must learn this art: to bring about in incantation, imagining and storytelling these nothings which every walk of life on this planet has personified in myth, tale, song, and poetry.

You will learn the art from the books I left you, and from other books that you-yourself must find.

Your friends will help you.

Remember child. As it was for the Merjans, the Scythians and our resistant dead so it is for us. This is why they fear us and haunt us down. They abhor vacuum, but for us it is everything. Therein resides the power of our magic against their magic. Our Orpheuses, Antigones and Medeas stand against their Prometheuses, their Creons and Presidents. You have always had it within you: the art, the mourning voice, and the magic. You must now look for it between the pages, among the stories told since the dawn of time in salvaged books and half-burned manuscripts. I shall talk to you through them. Soon you won't need me, you will fight your own battles and do your own writing. Poems and ballads will be written about you. They'll be sung and shouted from the hills and the rooftops of big halls. So that no one forgets your name. Soon. Now go. Your time is up. You must leap up from the floor and run.

Run, run like hell.

Before you do, tell me your name, your true name. I will keep it from them. Tell me girl, will you come to us? Will you escape from the night of the world?

4 Into the Night World

The first time that Hodoo Girl fell into the night of the world she was looking at her mother in the eye. And she looked into a night that became more terrifying and sorrowful as the years went by, when the grey mist began to creep into her mother's mind, clouding it, filling it with cut-up images of war, finance porn, and the glittering faces of the stars on television.

She must have been four years of age when it happened. It happened suddenly, as if the spark that was there one day had gone out of her mother's eyes without reason or explanation the next one.

A picture was taken around that time. In it appear her father, her mother, her sister and herself. Her father is sitting on a rocking chair in the small terrace of the flat they shared in one of the domed council estates now sealed off from the rest of London. Her sister is on the left of the rocking chair; she's staring at her father lovingly with both hands resting on his shoulders. The Hoodoo Girl appears at the right-hand corner, her head turned downwards looking at a huge map she has unfolded in front of her. Her father is looking at it, signalling a point in the map with the index of his left hand. Her mother is looking away, as if she did not belong there but outside the frame. With the index of her right hand she points at the Hoodoo Girl an accusing finger, a damning finger. In her face can be read a clear rictus of disgust.

This was about that time her mother stopped calling the Hoodoo Girl by her name. By year six, it was as if Hoodoo Girl had never been born, never existed. Her mother ignored her almost entirely until she was twelve, when the accusations began again: Hoodoo Girl had stolen money from her purse, Hoodoo Girl would turn the water heater up to thirty-eight degrees to watch mom burn her lips. Hoodoo Girl would replace the sugar with ground glass & roots in her tea. Once, her mother claimed to have seen the Hoodoo Girl standing by the side of her bathtub while she was in it with a plugged hairdryer in Hoodoo's hands.

On the day of Hoodoo Girl's fourteenth birthday her mother went to the nearest Autofaith police station, located in Kilburn High Road, and filed a complaint against her daughter on the grounds of vagrancy and heresy. Most damning, she denounced her as a reader, which was the gravest accusation that could be raised against anyone in New Britain. Reading had become a criminal offense among the youth after the re-enactment of the laws of treason of the Tudor era, in the wake of the fall of the world's economy sometime after The Great Pandemic in the early twenty-first century. In accordance with such laws, to wish for or imagine the death of the King, the demise of the financial heart of the globe in the City of London or the fall of the Church, and to host a migrant thought would be tantamount to committing high treason since only a step separates will and imagining from action.

To write about such things, to incite revolt against the City that sponsored the continuity of the monarchy once the latter renounced its claim to any part of the tax collection, or to raise doubts against the integrity of the Brex Church that had taken over the provision of most services after the latest and most radical wave of austerity measures became punishable with death.

To read about such things would carry a sentence of imprisonment or internment in one of the re-education camps that had been set around the country, on sites which were once university campuses.

Autofaith policemen had the responsibility to enforce the laws of treason. Agents dispersed among the population police trends and not yet widespread attitudes and fashions in an effort to foreclose possible futures. They wore no uniform, no badge and no identification bar an ornate electronic tattoo made out of gold in the shape of a shell, camouflaged somewhere in their bodies, for which they acquired the moniker 'rococoes.' Their job was to stop them treasonous imaginings before they could become widespread dangerous tendencies among the people. They did so with the help of fashion codes and so-called anti-punk regulations. Both autofaiths and rococoes responded neither to His Majesty's Government nor to the reinstated Parliament, but to an institution commonly known as The Arc, a common acronym for the All Religions Council.

The Arc emerged during the second decade of the twenty-first century after the governments of Europe finally ran out of money and the economy collapsed in the wake of Brexit and The Great Pandemic. At first, the three main churches united voluntarily in order to step in and fill the vacuum left by civil and public servants. They asked that, in return for their services, the main tenets of the world's organised religions be respected and followed to the letter by all media and expressed opinion.

When the Arc took control of culture and education, it began monitoring the content of syllabuses, reading lists and net streams in Britain and throughout the continent. It was only a matter of time before the Arc started correcting books, plays, and scripts it deemed inconvenient or disrespectful, pulling the plug on libraries, schools, universities, and literary gatherings, or boycotting publishing and streaming houses that refused to comply with the new guidelines. It was easier that previously thought. Britain already had the biggest number of unelected and religious figures sitting as state officials outside of Iran.

The new laws and standards were few and simple:

first, respect the people's right to observe the teachings of the church. Second, keep a vigilant eye for those who seek to interfere with the people's right to secure order and follow the teachings of the church; third, be ready to act in defence of such right out of your own will. Autofaith police began thus, as a voluntary force in the shape of Neighbourhood Watch. Rococoes were introduced later, as back up for the unmanned drones keeping order and security from the skies of London. Perhaps it is because of this reason that there are those who fantastically swear that autofaiths are not human. By the time the reinstated Parliament brought back the Tudor laws of treason, Autofaith had merged with all other law enforcement agencies of the state but remained a voluntary service and a private institution. Among its ranks were the equally feared and respected members of a highly secretive cross-religious order known simply as the New Inquisitors.

Nobody in their right mind would do anything to come across them. The Hoodoo Girl was just incredibly lucky that when her mother denounced her as both a heretic and a reader, the majority of the inquisitors were too busy planning their next move in the war that had broken out in the south of the continent, spreading from Syria into Greece, Iberia and France, to pay much attention. But one of them did notice, and when her mother returned home that day accompanied by the parish priest and an inquisitor witch, Hoodoo Girl's blood froze to icicles and her heart stopped.

She had never been in the presence of an inquisitor before and did not know what to expect. Her instinct told her she had to hide and at the first sign of peril run, run – run like hell.

Her father was no longer there to stand for her. He had gone, disappeared only a few days after the rocking chair portrait was taken. He did not say goodbye, provided no explanation, and left no note for her, which she always thought was very strange for a writer. "He has left us, the bastard," said her mother, "and we're much better this way." Hoodoo Girl's abuela, as she called her father's mother because of her Latinx indigenous origin, never believed it. "He must have had a very good reason to do what he did. She loved you, and wherever he is he's watching over you, waiting for the right moment to return," abuela said.

Such words rang hollow in Hoodoo Girl's ears, but in the back of her mind she always hoped that to be the case. Abuela had remained behind and stayed with them, much to her mother's annoyance, but she was now too ill and mostly bed ridden. That day, though, abuela summoned what must have been the last spark of light remaining in her sick body and stood up in front of the door to Hoodoo Girl's bedroom. She explained to the priest and the inquisitor how loneliness and grief had taken away la luz, the shine, out of the mind of her daughter-in-law, leaving instead a constant sadness that filled her like a black cloud, and asked them to forgive her terrible habit of coming up with incredible stories about her daughter. "She blames the girl for everything after her husband left. My son vanished, you see, leaving this poor soul behind," abuela said. "She never recovered. I pray for her and the girls every day. It is such a sad case, but nothing more than that, just a sad case that shouldn't concern you, one with which you must not waste your valued time."

The priest was convinced. After all, he knew abuela as a devout woman who never missed midday mass, a member of Mary's Legion and a strict South American Catholic. She had no inclination to lie, and no reason for doing so. Hoodoo Girl heard the priest apologising to the inquisitor from her hiding place under the bed. It was so hot and humid in there, a fact she attributed to the perennial rain now pouring down over London everyday and the eclipsed sun fixed behind the clouds in the middle of the sky. It was so hot that she began to feel at a loss for air.

When the door opened and the inquisitor entered the room, she thought she was going to choke and could feel her head about to explode. From her hiding place she could only see the end of the inquisitor's long black cloak and heard the cling clang sound of a silver chain as it hit the huge cross-like object that the dark priest carried on the waist as if it were a sword. The sound was so beats and bleeps and hypnotic that she could only conceive of it as the drumming beat that drummers and rococo followers describe as the result of their training in mysticism and the e-equipment they carry inside their heads.

Hoodoo Girl thought she could hear the inquisitor calling her name inside her head but dismiss it immediately as a consequence of her agitated state. Then she heard another voice, a familiar voice, compelling her to flee. "Get up. Do it now. There is no time. Run. Leap up from the floor and run. Run. Run like hell." The words kept pouring into her mind, an uninvited cascade of letters spoken from somewhere else, in another time, far away.

She saw the inquisitor's black-leathered clad hand raising the bed's cover. Focusing on the words being spoken by the voice from somewhere else, Hoodoo Girl closed her eyes. When she opened them, through the black veil that covered the inquisitor's face she saw a pair of blue eyes staring back at her, glowing in the dark. Hoodoo Girl would never forget them.

5 Callaloo

From those eyes, the night of the world lashed out, trying to steal her name and hide it in the depth of a mirror. Hoodoo Girl heard the words coming to her loud and clear. "I should have been there. I should have told you this story before, but I did not. I was blind and could not see, I was weak and could not reach you. The first day you went to school and no one knew you, but I wasn't there to explain why they all saw right through you. Yet it is not too late to save your mirror-soul from the coming darkness. I am here. I have come back to tell you: you still have a name. Don't look into her eyes. Don't let her see what is in your mirror. Listen to my voice. Get up. Do it now. There is no time. Run. Leap up from the floor and run. Run. Run like hell. All the world is around us, and looking to be changed."

Hoodoo Girl did as she was told. Once more, she closed her eyes.

Everything faded away. The inquisitor's eyes, the bed, the room, the flat, the estate, the dome, the heat and the pouring rain. The whole world and everything that is returned into this night. Hoodoo Girl fell into it as one may fall into a well or a dark cave in dreams and nightmares. She fell slowly, having enough time to look around. This world of black and blue shades had many rooms, many halls with many walls, many shelves, and many mirrors hanging from those walls. In the shelves there were hundreds or thousands of books, and on the side of the mirrors she saw many copies of the map her father had shown her when she was a girl, hung upon pegs. She took one of the mirrors, and a face appeared upon it. "Do you know my name?" asked the face in the mirror. "If you give me your name, I'll give you mine in exchange. Write it on the back of the frame, and I'll be yours and you'll be mine for all time." Hoodoo Girl turned the mirror and began to read the name written in gothic letters on the back. As she read every character, a cloud of black smoke began to take shape before her. The face in the mirror was now before her. "Break it, destroy the mirror and you shall free me. And I'll be eternally indebted to you, little girl," said the face in the cloud of black smoke. She did as she was told, and he smiled.

"This is a labyrinth," said the cloud. It is multiple and infinite not only in shape and form. Time here comes at a standstill. If you stay here, you may fall forever. Here, drink this", said the cloud giving Hoodoo Girl a little bottle containing a blue liquid. "What is it?" she asked. "Night juice. Sound," said the cloud: "it sharpens the imagination. If you drink it, the different parts of this dream will come together in an accidental relation the result of which is you. You will be that relation. It will be the I. It will be you. It'll make you free."

Hoodoo Girl drank it.

"Let your mind roam, let go of it relax and float downstream child," continued the cloud. "In its freedom, your imagination can dismember all manner of creatures and put them back together again. Like dolls made out of different parts abandoned and found. It can invent whole landscapes and forests made out of pieces of paper from old magazines, newspapers, and refused photographs. It tears everything apart and reconnects it in the most amazing manner. Whole worlds are born in this way, out of the power of images, cut-up, cut-ins, overlay and sequence. Go'n with yo'bad Self."

Hoodoo Girl noticed she had stopped falling. She was now in a large corridor, in what seemed like a metallic boat, a sub or a spaceship. She could see stars passing by through the portholes, planets, the lights of the buildings in the council estates of the south-east of London after a long night out at

The Victoria.

In such worlds, the law, if any, is that of arbitrarily associated ideas. In such worlds, everything is possible. Another end of the world is possible. If you were to imagine two separate things together, say a horse galloping up a hill and the wind blowing on your face, quite often you would picture yourself riding on the back of a horse up a hill in the West Country or below deck singing a love song in Middle Passage.

> "The westward pull of death,
> As slick white knives slit black throats..."

Oh, what a marvellous dreamlike feeling that is. We adults forget all about it and are the worse for it. That thing of wild imagining things called freedom. The children's imagination. And yet, now you also know this: that it is but an empty freedom. The kind of which can all too easily turn into a nightmare.

> For even though we are the sun's song
> The roar, the surge, the rhythm and the shock
> As the prophet says
> We must destroy
>   to live,
> as the poet says.
> The adult's imagination of a children's imagination.
>   With no clothes on.

6 Specters o' th' Night

You learned it the hard way. You learned it on that day when you looked into the eyes of your mother and realized she had been taken by the darkness. She couldn't recognise you, remember?

You said to her:

You are my mother! Not just any woman bearing a child in her arms but the one most familiar to me, and I must be to you since I came from you and I constantly remind myself of you!

You were so young back then, and I cannot even begin to imagine what that must have been like for you. Night Specters. If you remember that day, or if you want to remember it at all. That was the day the whole world turned night against you.

Vibrating black light.

I know you don't want to hear about these things. Not from me, of course. And yet, hear you must:

You are the Seventh Daughter of the Seven Daughter.

Descended from Drum.

From that which is first blown to form no longer known but thrown into the unknown.

You in The Zone.

Shown to be alone.

Lone Hoodoo Girl you may be reminded of these things through something else, so that merely the image of that day but not the day itself may be brought in upon you.

I know it already, I've seen it already, I've heard it all already.

Get off my case! You might say.

I constantly remind myself of her.

I don't merely hear her screams, I feel her anger, and

see her coming to me with the burning hot red poker in her hand.

Have I ever shown you my scars?

When I was fifteen, I began surrounding them with cut ins and cut ups, creating a flesh and blood landscape that to my eyes became a singular work of art. And I promised myself that as soon as I hit nineteen, I will have them covered in black and yellow and red ink tattoos. This is how I go within, into my inner imagination and self.

The Zone.

The cyclone.

There, I'm protected.

There, I cry alone.

There, she cannot enter.

I remind myself, and in doing so, free myself from these images. From the image of that day, which you push me to constantly remember. The day when I looked into her eyes and saw the night of the world.

There, I placed myself into myself. Her, for me, is that night in which I immersed both her and I as if we were both traversing the oceans inside a submarine boat and emerged on the other side at the entrance to the Garden. Both her and I. Her madness and mine. Wall Street is going to burn.

7   Wall Street's Gonna Burn

You said

> live on the web
>
> live on nbc

> > broadcasting gomorrah
> >
> > falling…

Wall Street's gonna burn

> > you said

all day

> on that day

the revolution was

> > televised

all day on that day

> the day you negated her.

The day you refused to continue to listen to her,

> as she shouted:

> You are not my girl!

> Not mine! Not of me!

To me you don't exist,

> you spy, you alien, you just burst out of me!

You must remember, if you want to remember,

> > that day

the day she went to The Ministry and denounced you as a spy

> a spook

a hoodoo

> > a terrorist.

The Ministry works confusing our rhythms. The Ministry:
its autofaith policeniaks,

> its civil informants,

---

* Credit to Larry Neal, 'Black Bogaloo' and 'Hoo Doo Hollerin' Bebop
Ghosts' for some of the lines sampled here.

its exorcists,

priestesses and priests,

an inquisitor
and a witch.

She was one of them.

Your own mother was of them.

An informant.

She fell under the influence of a priestess-inquisitor-witch.

Like so many among us.

It is because of them that we're now slaves of ourselves.

So many among us, out in a long queue as soon as the shops are open.

The Ministry tells the shop owners when to close and for how long.

So that we all get symptoms of withdrawal.

It is because of them that we're now slaves of ourselves.

Slaves of ourselves.

Such is The Ministry's motto.

The Ministry's office was located in Whitehall,

far from our council estate flat

in the north east of ex-London.

You couldn't fathom how your mother managed to get there, pass the checkpoints, the soldiers and the Autofaith police. Every other day, she would get lost trying to get sanctioned cigarettes from the corner shop. Every other day you and your sister would take turns to go searching for her. And yet, that day your mother found her way out of the domed council state.

That day
the day she went to The Ministry
and denounced you

as a spy

a spook

a hoodoo

a terrorist.

That day, it was your turn to go looking for her. Nobody else was at home that day, so you left to look out for you mother taking good care of locking all doors and windows to stop robbers and drummer gangs from stealing your precious doll collection.

It was unique,
        your collection.
None of the dolls
           were whole.
All of them broken
             alone
      & incomplete
Carefully,

you put them on the shelves one by one organised by size, eye colour or simply the point in time when you had come across them. They were made out of the discarded pieces of other dolls that you had found in the playground or thrown away in the garbage. You would bring them back home and nurse them with the same love and care other people nurse a stray cat or a dog. You would clean them up, fix them with glue & paint, and prepare chicken soup for them. If they were missing an eye, you would look for a replacement in your transparent Perspex plastic box full of eyes. Eyes of different colours and sizes: green eyes, blue eyes, brown eyes, purple eyes and your very favourite, wacky serpent white David Bowie eyes.

You chose that one, a white Bowie eye. It was the correct size. It had an uncannily dilated pupil. When the doll finally made it on top of the shelf you gave it a name: of course, Bowie.

You named her Commander of all the other dolls.
Forming small groups,
        to study the enemy.

Organise carefully
know yourselves
and those who come among you.
Destroy The Ministry
and their lackey running dogs.
Wall Street's gonna burn.
Study your ways
and the ways of the Beast Police,
the Autofaith Police.
Prepare for a war of dolls
liberation.
Doll power / every hour;
sisters unite
Without mothers, fathers & brothers.
What does it all mean?
The funk and boogaloo.
What does it mean?
Blow it.
Blow it all.
Blow change & revolution;
blow back;
blow black;
blow love.
Kick ass.
Kick Whitey's ass.
Then read him a poem telling him -
Father; Brother;
Mother; Witch;
The Ministry;-
why you did it
'For Whitey Will Say He Can Neither Know
Nor Understand'
As if he doesn't know why you did it.
Take over the poster boards.

Wake up one morning
The inquisitor's face staring you in the eyes
Her eyes.
Your eyes.
Bright Blues Eyes.
Your Big Doll.
Fist Clenched.
                    Power sign.
Paint it in the streets;
                    say it on the radio;
on television nbc;
          wall Street's gonna burn;
The City is going to burn;
          paint it bright sun-colours;
paint it black
          against the black asphalt.
Wall Street's gonna burn.
Paint it weird
          symbols and dancing signs;
the children of Birmingham;
the Bowie-eyed dolls of ex-London;
exploding;
          floating
          in the sky of that day
          the day you refused
          to continue to listen

                              to her,

                    to him,

               to me;
          instead you went to the sea
                    the sea dripping in chains;
And you saw the vision
          of the Nohor
                    the Slave ships

27

the cotton fields
the council state
the corrupt buildings of Westminster
the cops.
Wall Street & The City will burn.

Blow,
blow and dance and dazzle the beast with footwork.
Hoodoo footwork,
girl footwork.
Do you have a name Hoodoo Girl?

No, not your given name. The other name. The grafitti written behind your mirror-soul.

You cried long and hard waiting for your mother to come back from The Ministry that day. The day she denounced you

as a spy,
a spook,
a hoodoo,
a terrorist.

She told them you had been lured by one of the Pakistani boys who attend the nearby mosque on Kingsland Road. She told them she was scared of you, of your Qu'ran reciting, your veil wearing and your jihad chanting. She told them the darkness had taken hold of you. She told them you had threatened to fill the dolls you so carefully made & organised into small groups with zenade and mute explosives. She told them she was afraid you and your Pakistani boyfriend would show up at school and blow the whole damn place up,

in bright sun-colours
X-ploding;
floating
in the Sunday sky.

And they believed her.

8 Bowie

Next day, when you came back from school, you found the front door of the flat smashed into pieces. Your first thought was robbers, drummer gangs, and the sudden realization that you may have forgotten to lock the door. Your sister had not come back home the night before. And mother?

Taking a deep breath, you clutched the sputchstick you carried around in your bag. Nothing could have prepared you for what you found inside.

Because of her madness and my weakness, this mother thing has always counted for you as something essential and altogether different. For you, in the I that is her madness and your self it counts as a sign. And as sign, you already know it, your mother is her madness. This fact, this looking at her as a mere sign, as reflection in itself of all that was to come, that is your object, your life and desire. It is inwardness, the path you used in order to escape into imagination. The top shelf of dolls. Bowie. It served you well, it guarded you from the shouting, the blows, the hot red poker on your forearm, the black in your face and the blurred vision. It took away the pain. Bowie.

But now it must also enter into existence and become an object in the world out there. The world real. The world I told you about. The world I promised to show you. And even though I didn't keep my promise, let me say that all those worlds you have within you, this inwardness, this night, must be made external.

You must return to being and future past.

Do not worry. I cannot know what you must have gone through, all that you felt that day when you came back from school and you were tired because you had been looking for her the night before, and you were hungry because there was nothing left on the fridge and the shelves, and perhaps you forgot to close the door, and had forgotten to turn off the gas mains because it was way too cold, and God knows what she did when she came back with the Autofaith policemen on tow, if she had left all four stoves of the gas cooker open as well as the oven and why on earth they didn't perceive the smell, or whether it was just too late. Perhaps she lit a match as she always did to have a smoke, and then, and then, it was all fire and fireworks and horror and horror-show and there was talk of jihad and the devil and the Islamists in the estate.

The thing is, Bowie died.

She melted together with all the other dolls on the top shelf.

And what are you going to do now?

What are you going to do now?

Your whole world has gone up in flames.

9 Angel-Machines

Can I have a name,
>   mother? You said,
>   all the other kids have names.
>   You said.

But she refused
>   to give you one.
>   She would call
>   you
>   Little Girl
>   Hoodoo Girl.

She would speak of you as the small being living inside her head, gnawing on her entrails and eating her from within, ready to burst out. To give you a name would have meant conferring upon you substance and a life, something external and completely different from what you were when you were in, being looked at by her. To name you would have been to accept that you were there, that the world around you had consistence and that not everything was the consequence of a process of creation by some abstract super-being, or an after-effect of her overburdened imagination. That would have been too much.

She would have none of that.

And who can blame her? There were many like her in those days. Exiles of the spirit, inner migrants, itinerants of the mind fleeing from the devastation outside. Drummers, they call them. Sickos acting as if they had implants on their heads constantly playing the same beat, angel-machines escaping into their dome heavens to avoid being crumped to death.

You yourself used to say: I'm getting out of here one day. I mean it. You said. What the hell, even if you do get out it's no good' cause no matter how far you go they'll find you. They, inquisitors and Autofaith police. They'll fetch you back here. They'll shoot you.

    And if they don't

    then mumsie will bust you

        to pieces.

        Just ask me.

            A little night music.

ALAM

    DAM

        BANG

    DA DA

  DAM

ALAM

        DAM

    !

I lost a planet boy, missing a planet boy, bust you to pieces boy.

    Just ask me.

    The taste of blood. Smack. A broken lip. Bang. A bruised chest.

    Alam dam bang da da dam, alam dam!

    A hit on the head. A sudden rush of blood to the head. I'm leaving now, I'm getting out of here, you hear me! Oh, child. Oh, boy. Oh, girl. Who are you? What is your name? No, not your given name. But the one written graffiti-style behind you mirrorsoul mira-tu-sol.

    She says there's a small beastie nesting inside your head. She says you alien. You spy. You spic. You spik in glyph. You spook. You hoodoo. A terrorist hell-bent on fiery destruction. Not mine. I did not give birth to you, you just burst out of the hole between my legs. I could not, I should not. You're no child of mine, and you shall have no name of mine.

I'm sorry. I know how hard it must have been. I know. A sudden blow to the head. The music stops. The lights go dark.

I'm sorry.

I'm sorry;

I gave you a name.

10   Cookie-Monster Hoodie

That day you woke up with a pounding headache. You took off your pyjamas to change into your favourite track bottoms, Watchmen retro t-shirt and cookie-monster hoodie.

You cookie-monster hoodoo hoodie.

In the mirror, you saw the bruises on your chest and back. Ignore the pain. Forget the black eye. No matter. Nevermind.

You opened the door very slowly, sure not to make a sound. The coast is clear. She may have gone already. She may be sleeping off last night. Didn't hear her coming back. No new boyfriend on sight. Thank God. You still remember the last one.

Easy does it. Make your way to the kitchen as if walking on eggshells. You're hungry. Hadn't eaten much for a while. No matter. Nevermind. On the way back from school you bump into a group of drummers. They're shouting and taunting people outside of the soft-kebab joint. You have no sputchstick and no blade. Only the old .32 abuelo left behind. No matter. Nevermind. They surround you. Shouting and taunting. You get scared. But didn't show it. You found the old .32 in your bag. Point it at them. Recoil. It's a mic you idiots! You sang. Always do that when fear freezes your heart. Escape into song. Escape into chant. Feels like a trance.

Song saved your life.

That's a chief song-a-nota, said the tallest among them. You all right by us, little girl.

You the queen.

We foot soldiers.

You got away this time. Just another food expedition. Ghost-toast, chickpeas-for-self, a negated chunk of plasmeat, about a drum of liquid spirit, brown intuition rice, a box of associated ideas. No Kriskies. I can't take another expedition. You told yourself. The Mall is on the other side of the dome. Let a wandering satellite fall on my head right now. And transparent lentils plus a tube of quick-quack on your smashed head. The fiver you'd buried in the plant on the ledge outside the window was still there. You must remember this hiding place. It will do. Five pound-credits decorated with the face of some uber-Russian trillionaire. It should be enough to get some of the things on the list. You're good at avoiding drummers and taking all the back streets. You're good at this surviving shit. It's all about being street-neat and ready to run by two thirty, catch the tube at two forty- five, hide from the ticket agents, pass the checkpoint, and make it to the O2 Mall by three fifteen. From there, things often get easier.

If you hit the streets at two thirty, catch the ultra-tube at two forty-five, if you run like hell from them drummers and checkpoint policeniaks you'll make it. Bring your coupons, blade, and sputchstick. The old .32 calibre. Shoot and sing. You all right by us drummers. You our pet celebrity, singing little Hoodoo Girl. You the Queen. You gotta make it outta here. Run, pet. Run, run like hell.

Looks like you are wearing enough insurance. Looks like you have it all figured out. How to dodge them drum gangs, policeniaks, and inquisitor checkpoints. A couple of sputchsticks, a blade, a mute grenade, steel-pointed Doc Martens, a tube of gunk'a'duda to cover the bruise on your left eye, shades on. Menacing looking. Packing heat.

What's the story with the old pistol, morning glory?

It belonged to abuelo. He brought it from the Caribbean. From Colombia. You always wondered. Why on earth they changed their land of lush greenery and slow-motion sun for the grey god-forsaken Brexit island? Abuelo looked beautiful in pictures. Always a smiling face, which you can barely remember. He taught you how to dance when you were four. He taught the neighbours how to dance. He taught the whole damn state to dance.

That was before they said he was sleeping around with their white wives. They kicked the hell out of him. End of the story.

After he died, abuela found the .32 gun wrapped around some old newspapers from the time of La Violencia, when he was a clerk with the Prosecutor's office back in Colombia. The newspapers told the story of the last case he worked on. A mass grave filled with the bodies of women and girls. They had been raped and hung up from posts and shot point blank as a message for the peasants by paramilitary forces at the behest of their palm oil landowning masters. Abuelo left. He had to. Run. Run like hell. He brought the gun and the papers from the time of La Violencia with him. After he passed, abuela took the gun and broke it into two hundred small pieces with the help of metal file and iron saw. You saw her doing that every afternoon, while out there it rained lead and heavy metals.

Two hundred small pieces.

It took her a whole year to break it. She would put the pieces in her handkerchief and throw them one by one pieces in the garbage on the way to mass. No one knew. No one noticed. Except you. You took the pieces one by one and put them back together again with gunk, glue and glass tape.

12 Story of Prince Sun and Princess Moon

Abuela used to tell you the story of Prince Sun and Princess Moon.

They were enthralled with one another. But they could never meet in the sky high as Sun could only come out during the day and Moon at night. One night, Prince Sun escaped the guard's watch and came out to look at Princess Moon's reflection in the water. But his light so bright alerted the guardians in the sky. They came down to fetch him, intent on imprisoning Sun in Queen Death's cave forever. Princess Moon came down from the night sky to save her beloved Sun. She covered him with her naked body distracting the guardians with her beauty before they could get him.

"What is that light shining so bright behind you?" they asked.

"It's called an eclipse," she replied, and they left.

Whenever an eclipse occurs, it's Prince Sun and Princess Moon making sweet love to each other high up in the sky.

13 | Nevermind

That day you woke up with a pounding headache and bruises all over.

You ignored them.

No matter.

Nevermind.

After school, you went on a food expedition. When you came back home having dodged the gang of drummers, you were thinking about the story of Prince Sun and Princess Moon. When the eclipse passed, you found yourself before the front door of the flat, smashed into pieces. You clutched your old .32 sputchstick put together with paint and glue. Then you entered.

Nothing could have prepared you for you what you saw inside.

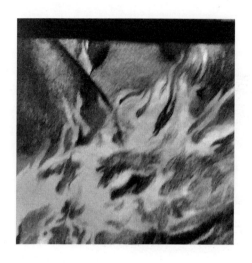

14 Voice in the Fire

You wanted to go inside looking for Bowie but abuela wouldn't let you. Too late, she said. Too dangerous, she said. They're here, she said.

This is the day your mother brought back a priest to get rid of the devil inside you.

You ran into your room. abuela stood on the front door between you and them. Mighty abuela stood there and no one would move her. Not your mother. Not the pigs. Not the priest. Not the inquisitor. When the riot policeniaks threatened abuela with her batons you appeared from behind both hands holding the .32 puzzle-gun, pointing at them. abuela shouted "no!" and started crying. She took the gun and hugged you. They wacked her on the head. When she passed out you knew you were all alone. Fetched Bowie and hid under the bed.

It's too late. Too dangerous. She's here.

She found you.

I don't know how but I know it's my fault. She found you. Took you from under the bed, knocked you down, and now sits on top of you carving your chest with her fingernails. She wants your mirror she wants your soul. Mirrorsoul. Tu so(u)l. Tu sol. Her glowing blue eyes peering at you, drilling your skull. You look back and your song turns into chant and the chant into a shriek and everything fades away. You look into her eyes and it all goes away. This place, the howling wind, the black cloud of dead souls descending on you and your friends as you try to escape. Daylight fades away. Life fades away. The void a vanishing point.

It burns.

The voice in the fire
    burns.

The flames spread quickly into the other bedrooms. The heat wave mowing down everything on its way.

You were saying thanks to abuela's ghost when your sister turned up, running towards you from the next building. Mom? She asked. Mom's gone, you said. Now it's just the two of us. You cried, but you couldn't figure out why were you crying for.

You couldn't have known that three other explosions preceded the one in your flat, between the late afternoon and the early evening of that day. You couldn't have known that by the time you hit the ground some thirty two residents of the estate had died already, murdered in unknown circumstances, and that so much speculation would be caused by the apparent abduction of thirteen children, including you, aged fifteen, and your 17-year old sister.

You ran like hell.

Speaking in front of the TV cameras a few hours after another explosion had claimed the lives of at least two dozen more, the police commissioner spoke of people having been caught unawares, caught sleep, caught dreaming of holidays in Spain and having sex with retro-Katie Price lookalikes. Caught unawares. Or caught in the act.

The total number of the dead quickly rose to the thousands in the next few days. Terrorists? A plague? A plague by terrorists. The Russians? The Chinese?

Of course, you knew nothing about all this. You couldn't have known. You were running. Running like hell.

Permanent Minister Johnson appeared before Parliament two days later. He spoke of criminals, fanatics, assassins. Wreckers. Little is known yet about the wrecker's motives and their identities. But we all know people like that need no motives and have no identity other than the one given to them by their fanatic beliefs, leaders and handlers, he said. We know the police and Autofaith had been conducting undercover operations for some time in the domed Council Estates north east of ex-London. Popham Council Estate was first on the list of the intelligence services, God bless them and their thought-listening software, for it was suspected that a sleeper cell of Islamists had been operating there. Recruiting among the disaffected youth. Feeding to them a rhetoric of class hatred and disloyalty to blood and land and nation.

I have been informed by the Police Commissioner, PM Johnson told Parliament, of their suspicions: that one or many of these cells detonated home-made explosive charges in at least seven key areas within the dome estate, killing hundreds, perhaps thousands of their trusting families and neighbours as well as the police officers who sacrificed their lives in the name of duty and to protect our freedoms.

To protect our freedoms.

In the name of His Majesty's government, he said, let me express our heartfelt condolences to the families of these honest men, their widows and the orphans they have left behind; for they will surely suffer as much as the thirteen or so children that disappeared two nights ago from Popham Estate. We believe some of them may have been abducted, possibly taken out of the country to be indoctrinated in the madrassas of continental Europe and the Middle East, and later on recruited to come back home and commit atrocities such as the one that took place in Popham Estate two nights before. The chief of the intelligence services working together with the Council and Autofaith has informed me that the possibility of a foreign hand cannot be dismissed. The evidence points towards the puppet government of Tehran and their masters in Beijing, who may have ordered this attack as an act of retaliation over the sanctions ordered by this Permanent Cabinet in accordance with the instructions issued by the Council of the Non-United States. The governments of the Islamic Republic of Iran and the peoples' Republic of China will have to respond for the loss of lives in British soil; this is an act of war against the Reunited Kingdom & Republic of Great Britain. So said the Permanent Minister during the emergency meeting of Parliament held two days before the explosions.

So said we all.

15 Popham Estate Massacre

The press called it Popham Estate Massacre. During the weeks following in its wake, numerous TV agencies around the world dedicated their coverage to describe in as much detail as possible the lives of the thirty-two initial victims of that day. Including your mother. There were hagiographies written in the printed press about the undercover Autofaith police officers who gave their life for the security of the kingdom and republic. A state funeral was planned, which took place at Westminster Abbey, an unprecedented occurrence credited to His People's Majesty himself. The people of ex-London and the Central City of London came out in droves to fill the streets adjacent to the cathedral. The outpour of emotions only matched by the general outcry captured on camera, on the web and in wetware newstrips around the globe.

King Harry the Diverse pronounced the homily. In it he praised the work of the security services and spoke of the firmness of his beliefs against the dark forces of religious intolerance coming from southern Europe and the Arab world. It had more viewers around the world than his first wedding some fifty years ago.

And despite the protestations of innocence made by the Iranian ambassador on the floor of the United Nations, Britain and its NATO allies, led by the pro-consular administration of the Non-United States passed a Resolution paving the way for a military response to the aggression irrespective of a Chinese veto. Speeches were made in the hall of the UN Security Council, with the Picasso painting that commemorates the victims of the bombardment of the Spanish city of Guernica covered over with a large black cloth to fit the mise-en-scene favoured by TV and PR crews. Communications were exchanged. Further resolutions were written, including one supported by the Council of World Religions, which gathered representatives from the reformed churches of Islam. It was all a matter of language and communications, as it is the case with everything that returns to being.

The Enlightenment Wars they called them. The War Against Darkness. Such is comms & language, the name-giving power.

But you were oblivious to all this. You did not read the papers and you did not watch the news. Like most of the population in New Britain and elsewhere you had forgotten how to read and cared nothing for the stories that journalists told in the news. And so, you never learned that your mom had apparently died a national hero, buried at Westminster, her coffin covered in the Union Jack being followed by cameras from the four corners of this god-forsaken world.

Such is comms & language, the name-giving power.

You didn't read about these things, for you pretended not to know how to read. It would have been unwise to do otherwise. Never mind the fact that you have been taught when you were a child. You didn't know why or what for, and always kept it from others; not even your sister knew. It was better this way, to pretend you couldn't have known. You were out in a shopping expedition.

Lucky you.

16   Age of Spectacle ($)

This is the Golden Era of Intelligent Machines and Television.

This is the Age of Spectacle.

Prosthetic lenses inside your eye and implanted smart phones feed all narratives and images downloading them straight from the world wide web into your brain.

An apotheosis of spectacular visage and duck faces.

Spectacle triumphant.

In it we trust.

Those of us stupid enough, antiquated enough, old enough to cling on to the magical power of words and illuminations printed in books did so in knowledge and disavowal of the fact that we were a dying breed.

Like dinosaurs hoping an asteroid would change its course.

We believed we were writing after the end of literature.

Like everybody else, we were merely sketching visual images.

The thought of the end was merely a symptom.

The images of the world were merely a symptom.

The phenomena of the world were merely a symptom.

As such, they were like spells and untimely hieroglyphs.

Meant to be deciphered.

They present themselves to us like the words in these pages.

Allusive and elusive.

Ready at hand.

Yet they vanish the moment you touch them.

Better to write them on the back of mirrors.

Bring them back to life.

Better to eat them.

Eat them words.

Munch on them words.

Like ritual palabreros chewing coca leaves and the enemy's words.

Don't be afraid to push them to the point where they vanish,

or become paradoxical.

For these are oral teachings.

And the images passed in such manner shall raise your unconscious.

They get stored in the backroom of the mind, its dark warehouse.

Its night.

The night of the world.

And from there, in their empty nothingness and simplicity.

These words and images absorb everything and contain it.

Like idols and fetishes and icons,

books and films and stories are button ties.

Botones de nacar.

Meant to quilt together definitive formulations of some ideas and spells,

or merely sketching the outlines of others.

For you to reinvent and develop.

Elsewhere,

    at sea;

The sea of your unconscious in the Golden Age of television.

The sea of your split unconscious in the Golden Age of Television.

Split

    spliced

split

spliced
div
ided.
Made up
div
ided.
Neither fully alive nor totally dead.
Frankenstein's creature.
A zombie.
A cyborg.
Division.
Separation.
Fragmentation.
Partition.
Atomization.
Division.
And defence.
Ichspaltung, he said.
A spell, he said.
A graph, he said.
$

A process of division set in motion by a drawing or a spell.

Must be understood as splitting and splicing and dividing.

Thereby bringing them back to life.
A zombie.
Frankenstein's creature.
A cyborg.
The disappeared.
Neither fully alive nor totally dead.
Cut
paste.
Cut-up

cut-in.

And overlays in the Golden Age of television.

For there is a wealth of images in the Golden Age of Television:

Here a bloody head shoots up,

                there a torso,

       a severed arm,

a blood splatter against the white walls and corridors of Popham Estate.

Such is the night.

The inner side of human nature existing here, in our/ selves.

We humans have become creatures of the night,

blinded by the light of a thousand screens.

For this light gives you only the empty form.

The void a vanishing point.

True likenesses,

      on the other hand,

            bring your inner workings out

                in the open

and make the internal be

                or let the outside in.

And from the outside of this living labour,

            this pauper of the person,

     this body,

        a negation

           it transcends

           the totality

             of god and its riches

     this living labour of love;

            creation

        absorbed

           in work

and its theft by those who shall be your Masters.

They're the enemies
        whose words
        you shall learn to chew
                spit
                spell
                split
                splice.
For then
only then,
once you give the image a proper name
        write about it,
                on the back of a mirror,
        then
        only then
both the girl and the image of the girl
                become the most powerful unity.
Your true spirit and being.
This is why your mother never dared pronouncing
your name.
        She sensed that words and names,
                when added to the likely images
                        that come before them,
                        become present vehicles
                        for the convocation
                        the transmission of magical forces.
As if an utterance,
                or the writing of a page
        the drawing of a face,
                out of nothingness
were enough to effect changes in the outer world.
And bring about other worlds.
The many worlds that because of you exist in this one.
She was,
        in her own way,

a savage philosopher
for whom your name had become taboo.
Not a thing,
          but a condition.
                         Having a name,
you are something entirely different
          from what you are when looked at
          by other people.
                              You are not merely what they see.
You are Hoodoo Girl,
          not a thing,
                    but a relation,
                         a condition.
You are being and existence.
"I'm Hoodoo Girl. I've got six mute grenades, a blade
and my old .32 sputchstick.
Today,
          I'm getting outta here.
          And I'm taking my sister with me.
We will dodge drangstorms,
                    drummers,
                    inquisitors,
                    Autofaith policeniaks.
She can shout all she wants.
It's only out of fear that she shouts.
Fear of my being and my very existence.
No longer a girl: a woman.
Time to go.
          Time to run.
Run.
          Run like hell.
And to hell with anyone trying to stop us.

17 Hau

By means of this name, your true name, a word and a likely likeness, the thing that has been born out of the night emerges as a being charged with power. Your ancestors called the thing *hau*. They called it *mana*. It can take the shape of a flower that grows in the place of cadavers, protected by the shadow of the oldest trees in the Amazon rainforest. It passes back and forth between the animate and inanimate worlds, and it is the primal source of all creativity.

In the Garden, Ma'at, first, and then Lilith or Eve, named all things. It was their sovereign right as spirits, a sort of primal receptivity of all nature or its recreation, out of spirit and mind itself.

It is your right now. You have image, language and name. A mirror-soul. Hoodoo Girl You have become Taboo.

Sacred and forbidden.

Not a thing, but a condition.

18 Mana

Now that you have acquired a true likeness, name and language you also have within you the sun and the moon. You can shine bright in the night sky and lead the way back to the garden.

You're electricity in motion.

Mana.

Mana is electricity in motion.

All people carry it, but most of us chose to forget about it in order to blend in.

Those who do not, end up carrying and absorbing the mana of others. That is why in the past they became founders and rulers of cities, kingdoms and black republics. They carry an excess of mana. So do their fetishes, their true likenesses, words and writings.

Such energy can be transmitted through the utterance of names, for it is a fundamental point of our savage philosophy that true images, words and signs have a physical connection with things. Unlike fake idols and false promises. Anyone who has carried the power to recreate the world anew, out of spirit, has taken this fact seriously. As did Ma'at, Lilith and Eve, so did Isis and Artemis, Circe and Medea, Venus and Ixchel, Oshun and Tayira maíz blanco y frijoles negros.

So will you.

This is the secret: the link between a name and the image, the thing or the person named is not merely an arbitrary or ideal association, but a determinant chance. Areal and substantial connection uniting the two.

Our ancestors knew this, which is why they spent more than five hundred years of inexistence waiting for the return of Venus, summoning enough *mana* to free themselves from the name that was imposed on them.

Just like Caliban was given a name by the magus Prospero, who thereby gained dominion upon him.

So as to be able to visualize and name again.

If you forget this, it will happen to your people what already happened to our people, the people of Macondo when they were mowed down by the dreaded insomnia plague. At first, they were comfortable in their jet-lagged television state. One of them, whose name has been lost, said: "that way we can get more out of life!" He was wrong and passed away. Soon enough, the plagued forgot how to dream. They could no longer see, and they could no more imagine so they lost their memory utterly and completely. Time vanished. Thereafter, nothing else ever happened in Macondo. They also forgot the names of things. It was the night of the world.

It fell like viral fog upon them.

It is said the village was swept away by the tempest they called Progress. There is now a maze in the maize fields where once was the village of Macondo. It is there to remind us how fragile memory is, and to re-enact and renew our vows: that for as long as there is image and language time will continue to pass, for we're of it, in it and we make it. We are the guardians of this magic, of time, true images and language.

For we're of it, in it and we make it.

Paused Images

In the light of truthfulness and language the world is no longer a realm of paused images and shadows. No more the image of cavernous Popham Council Estate paused in CCTV cameras, the air-conditioned nightmare and the killings.

I know.

Nothing could have prepared for what you saw that day.

What was found in CCTV cameras and forensic news reports.

It's grim.

"The image is paused, grainy and low resolution like perpetual snowfall. Thankfully, there is no soundtrack, and one is glad that none is necessary. The camera work is minimalist, which perfectly suits its subject. The white walls and seemingly infinite corridors of Popham Council Estate provoke the uncanny feeling of being trapped inside a maze. Or in a dream of thousand rooms. At other times, the images recall the feeling of glass and Formica laboratories where genetic experiments are being conducted to obtain a hybrid between human and alien life forms. The place is drenched in an intense white light and void of human presence, except for a casual operator dressed from head to toe in an inflatable isolation suit watching the blue numbers that drip like rain in a huge screen console, writing them down on his tablet. The camera pans over the solitary corridors. Not a soul in sight until it stops by the gatehouse that controlled access to the Estate. Over the magnetic reader used by the inhabitants of Popham to present their ID wet ware in order to exit or enter, there can be seen the clear marks of five fingers made in blindingly bright red blood. The camera turns to show the face of an Autofaith agent putting on the helmet of his isolation suit. The three roaring lions' emblem of the agency is emblazoned on his white t-shirt, together with its official name: New National Health Service. According to witness testimonies, the first units to arrive in the scene got there less than three minutes from the time an emergency call came from within the compound. They described smoke and debris still falling from above, like perpetual snowfall, while half-burnt people, a few survivors, walked around like zombies, like Frankenstein's creature, like cyborgs numbed by the force of the last explosion. But none of this is captured in the video. Instead, the camera zooms in on the face of the young Autofaith forensic investigator. He points to the blood markings on the door, which then opens up to reveal the interior of the gatehouse. The image jumps. Now captured by camera number two from inside the corridor, the image leads to the gatehouse and the magnetic reader. At first, what appears to be a black ink blot covers the entire floor of the corridor. It takes a while to realize it is blood. Here, a severed head shoots up; there, a bloody hand still clinging to the gate's handle, trying desperately to pass an ID wet ware card through the magnetic reader. No use. As soon as the sensors picked up the heat and radiation, or whatever it was that activated them, all entrances and gates separating the different levels of the estate, and it from the outside world, went into lockdown and all leaving privileges were revoked. There are body parts, but no whole bodies. They have gone away, vaporised by the energy wave of the blast. The other images are shadows of absent bodies left behind on the walls by the energy of the blast. Hiroshima and Nagasaki all over again in Popham Council Estate. But everything else seems heavenly and unperturbed. The high-grade security glass of the windows was made to withstand zenade blasts, white missile fire and super-calibre bullets. It was not meant to protect the inhabitants of the estate from the violence out there, but on the contrary, to impede a stray missile such as the ones fired in one of the casual gang battles inside to harm the good people of the Central City of London driving pass the estate on their way to the airport on Boris Island. There is a pile of papers still perfectly positioned on the corner of a desk inside the gatehouse. Leaflets for the concert of app music artist Ice Ten. It was to be a homecoming concert. Legend has it the band's leader, DJ Resident, had been born and grew up in the state. He got out. If he did, so can others. Ice Ten were famous for their rendition of 'I Am a Missing Planet Boy'. Their back catalogue also features 'Angela Davis for Queen', 'Sun Ra for President', and 'Kenyatta for Minister of Defence'. The concert got cancelled, replaced by a charity event. Camera Three shows twelve bodies inside flat number five. Two of them are on the lower left hand corner of the apartment, lying on the floor, blown up, one of them with a cracked up head, eyes wide open and a wound to the chest so deep it fuses with the blackness of the charred remains on its right hand side. The two bodies must have been fused into one by the heat wave. The other, also charred, eyes wide open, seems to stretch her arms to the heavens. Her mouth is wide open, as if she were screaming, begging for mercy. Perhaps this poor soul did pray for help from above in that last minute. Maybe she did see an angel coming down; the angel would have liked to stay and help but a violent gust propelled him forwards so he could do nothing else but contemplate the unfolding catastrophe and debris. Or else, this was the Angel of Death, falling from the skies with his legions to finish off this rabble with his sword of fire. Perhaps this video has captured the fall of Sodom and Gomorrah. The violent gust they call Progress. All the corpses are badly burnt, four of them at the centre of the scene, blackened, their remains encased into the walls. Two more can be seen in vertical position, as if they were standing up at the moment of the explosion and the force of the impact had merely interrupted their conversation. These ones died right there, their backs against the white wall, their burnt bodies surrounded by a sort of full body halo coloured in different shades of grey. There's another corpse on the right-hand corner. It appears to be seated, his body in some sort of yoga position, arms crossed over the lap. But it was not really seating. Rather, the legs have collapsed, having been turned into ash. Only the torso remains. The face, although severely burnt is still recognisable. The flesh still adorned with its natural colour. This victim was not facing in the direction of the blast and did not see it coming. She did not even notice it. Which is bizarre. Perhaps the terrorist used the latest version of home-made mute grenades that are supposed to make no sound as they explode. Three other bodies can be seen in the back. This time, the scene reminds us of those films about the divine punishment that befell the city of Pompeii, or the fall of the Wall of Jericho. Just as it happened then, people here were caught unawares. They were going about their own day-to-day business when the mutenades went off. At least three of them, perfectly timed one after the other, placed in flats five, ten and twenty-seven. The disturbing sight of charred remains distracts one from the obvious. In flat ten, the same as in flat five and in the gatehouse, all surrounding furniture, papers and décor remain in perfect order, the objects almost untouched, whole and unharmed, but for a few marks of smoke and fire here and there. Consider the dinner table in flat ten. It looks as if it had just been prepared, food still served on the plates. There's an antiseptic quality to the whole scene, as if some sort of carefully selective weapon hit the people but not the objects. What kind of explosive can do that? None I know of. Which contradicts the theory that these were home-made zenades or mute grenades. In fact, if asked, I would say the government has finally managed to rid this prison house of its most dangerous inmates by replacing them with the cast of Stepford Wives. The camera shows that the TV is still on in flat ten. In front of it, two blackened corpses with eyes wide open continue to watch the final round of the Great British Bake Off. The police camera turns around this couple: Ziddy Ibn Sharam, shopkeeper and poet, mid-thirties, of Indian or Bangladeshi origin sits comfortably on the right hand of the sofa, his hand still holding a fork over his microwave TV dinner. His head leans slightly forwards as if to catch the last fleeting flavour from the preparations of the show contestants. His shirt is unbuttoned, allowing the viewer to spend time on his protuberant mid-riff. His clothes are stained because of the ash, but otherwise remain in perfect condition as if the body had been burnt from the inside out affecting the tissue but stopping short of consuming the victims' attire or the trail on his lap. The curry is still piping hot and flavoursome. He wears no trousers. The woman on his side is a neighbour, Katherine Mamdem, unemployed for the last six years, out of benefits the last two. According to the government's records she had three kids aged ten, thirteen, and seventeen, loved soap operas and talent shows. She is naked. Several complaints have been filed against Mr. Sharam in the weeks prior to the incident for disturbing the peace of his neighbours, like playing loud music until the early hours of the morning and selling drugs wrapped within verses of poetry. No investigation was ever opened. The camera moves on to the main bedroom. Two bodies can be seen leaning against a small wooden table. There are four or five wads of cash perfectly piled up, a shotgun, two semi-automatic weapons, some seven bags of pills and three clearly visible Metropolitan Police credentials. The men died while counting the money and distributing the pills. The cash remains intact, the pills distributed into four groups according to their colour: red on the left side, then green, blue, and finally yellow on the right. It looks tidy, coherent and organised. A bureaucrat's paradise. But the bodies are horribly disfigured. The camera stops to reveal the deep head wound to the head of former PC Robert Garland. There are no obvious signs of explosion in this apartment. There are two other bodies in the room, on the bed to the side of the men sitting on the table. One of them was identified as belonging to 26-year old Maria Englund, of Russian origin. She is naked, turned upside down on top of the bed, her legs are blackened up to her knees, but the rest of her body seems untouched by the fire. There are blue and yellow pills on the bedside table and a broken glass. The video shows two Autofaith officers in protective gear turning the body on its back to show the face. She must have been a handsome woman, but her expression is terrifying. She worked as a hairdresser in one of the exclusive male-only salons in the West End, which granted her safe passage into Central City. According to the neighbours she kept to herself and took care of her 11-year old daughter alone. The girl disappeared, just like the other kids. Now the camera zooms in on Mrs Englund's abdomen. The word 'run' was carved on it. The autopsy revealed she had been raped several times with a broomstick. The wooden handle had been broken into two, one half used to carve the word in her stomach, the other half inserted in the rectum of the other body lying on the bed, burnt enough so as to make it unrecognisable. Dental and DNA records showed this to be the body of the youngest of the four policemen working undercover to infiltrate the alleged terrorist cell that operated out of Popham. Given the bloodstains found in the bathroom and the floor it was possible to establish that he had had been killed in the bathroom with the broomstick, then dragged and put on the bed over the body of Maria Englund before the killer, or killers, set the place on fire."

End of report.

But the video contained seven minutes more footage. These showed the camera leaving flat ten behind and continuing for what seems a very long time through corridors drenched in white light. Following empty staircases and rat-infested halls, until it finally reaches the door of flat twenty-seven. It was smashed into pieces. This is where you lived, together with your mother and your sister.

20 Whisper

The night before these horrible events your mother had a recurrent nightmare. She dreamt of you standing beside her bed, covered in flames. You took her hand in your hands, kneeled down, and brought your lips close to hear ears. Then you whispered: mother, can't you see I'm burning? Then, she woke up screaming, covered in sweat only to discover the flat set ablaze. She was inhaling smoke, fighting for dear life but the strength of the blue, red, yellow and green pills kept her half-asleep. Or perhaps she didn't really want to wake up. At some point, the heat and the fumes became too much, and she finally snapped back into reality. Or was it the opposite? Reality was too much and she snapped back into dream. Or else, it could be that what she encountered in the dream was much too powerful, even more unbearable that being torched alive. Who knows? Do you?

21   Blackened

In the additional seven minutes of footage her room appears completely blackened. Unlike the other places, here nothing survived. Not the pantheon of saints. Not the pictures of your abuela and Virgin Mary. Not the stack of bibles. Her body is seen fused to the ceiling above the bed. As if she had been lifted from it and swallowed by a sea of flames coming from the roof of the apartment. The investigators theorised this must have been the site of the first explosion, with the device having been activated right under her bed. But how does that account for the fact, clearly shown in the video, that her bed was in one piece? To add dramatic effect, Autofaith would come up with the story that your mother was out looking for her little girl, perhaps already captured or recruited by the terrorist gang. She had gone to the undercover policemen who dutifully informed their headquarters and having no consideration for their own lives began looking in the surrounding flats. Back-up arrived then and went into the flat with your mother when the device went off.

A tragedy. Thirty-two dead in the first explosion. Hundreds or even thousands more in the days that followed. Rioting and all.

And all the children of the households involved, all thirteen of them gone, including you and your sister. Seemingly vanished into thin air, the scenes of abduction missed by the cameras.

Who could have done such a thing?

22   Facing the Firing Squad

Many years later, when facing the firing squad, you would slip into a dream of your own. In the dream you were an old woman surrounded by your loved ones. Content, you would tell your grandsons and granddaughters stories of the war, of your time in prison, of the island of slaves and the quest for The Garden, and of the day when you were taken behind the barracks and faced the firing squad. Your hunger was gone. Your thirst was quenched. The fire in your mirror-soul had subsided. All your stories had been told.

Then, you would hear the voice of your mother. The same way she used to come to you every morning before sending you off to another boring day at school. The scolding and the shouting would seem to go on forever. Like time had been abolished. With a clear beginning but no ending, no before, no during, and no after. There was a singular timelessness and ubiquity that placed that day outside the normal range of comprehension, of recounting and mastery.

It felt like been trapped inside a maze, in the dream place of infinite rooms or in the foreverness created by two mirrors placed each one in front of the other. Not a room of your own, but the prison house of words in which Scheherazade locked herself in to escape execution.

At that moment, and perhaps for the first time in your life you would see it all very clearly. You had all time in the world to look at things without having to name them. All the time. There was no need to move, no need to escape or travel the oceans, for in there you occupied all places at once. You looked at the world around you, all the objects of the world and all the moments of your life with unparalleled understanding. A parallax, nothing was hidden from you.

The looked-at world was evanescent. The whole of it

sheltered, protected by one simple atmosphere. You breathed the air of this coloured and persistent landscape that evoked your childhood holidays in Foxham-near-Chippenham, with its morning routine of cereals in the larder with your cousins before going up the barn to help cleaning the horses. The smell of manure, the sheep running towards you, green apples falling from the trees, potholes of water from the rain the night before.

You and your cousins would ride on the back of Raindrops, your favourite horse, and fed him strawberries with sugar against the advice of your mother. The summer sun shining over the fields of Wiltshire, caressing your skin as you laid down on your backs and held each other's hands, secure in the feeling that this moment would never end.

Another apple would fall from the tree nearby the swings and the slide. Clump. Dump. Bump. You picked it up and put it in the bucket together with the others. Later on, auntie Imogen would make crumble and custard. You would breath in, inhaling the simple atmosphere of those days in Summerleaze. The aroma, the simple individuality of a slice of apple crumble drowned in custard. The wild berries. Cantering on the back of Raindrops. Feeding Albert. Cleaning the barn. All these moments rose out of one simple breathing raising up in the air and into a higher spiritual plane. Laying down on your backs, staring at the sun, holding hands, forever.

Remember the day you got lost in the field? Your mother was mad because she had to go back to work. So, she left you behind. When you came back, she told you off, shouting, kicking and screaming. She locked you up all day next day in the larder, sharing horse oats with the cockroaches. Just because you girls lifted off the ground, your spirits sliding over the fields of Foxham and saw yourselves seeing yourselves from the ground, surrounded by a canopy of white and yellow flowers.

Look at the horses galloping on their own. The sheep running scared because auntie Melissa comes with scissors. Look at yourselves going back the house in the old tractor. See Granma Gillian. These were no memories of the past but an eternal now proceeding through without completion. Your mother would come to you as she did always in the morning. Shouting, kicking and screaming. But your time is up. No getting up this time. Non running. No hell. Hell is behind. You are back from the war. You completed your quest. You are well fed, happy having told all your stories to the family.

Suddenly you heard her voice shouting: wake up!

When you opened your eyes, the firing squad was still there.

23 Newslavery

Get up.

Run.

Run like hell.

It's 4:27 a.m.

You must have reached the Hoopway already. You have to be at the tube station before 4:35 a.m. if you don't want to miss the train. You can't wait for the 7:30 a.m. to Central London. The third explosion will occur in exactly seven minutes. Three more between 5:35 a.m. and 7:00 a.m. in Portcullis House, Westminster, and nearby in Parliament Square. One of them killing the Peoples' Permanent Minister, Louis Boris Winston de Pfeffel Napoleon, three members of his staff (including his young assistant and lover, who had taken pictures of both of them going at it like rabbits the night before and was about to sell them to the tabloid press), four agents of his security detachment, three other members of Parliament, and over two hundred civilians.

The last three explosions, mimicking those at Popham, were to take place around 7:35 a.m. Those would be the deadliest, creating a cascade of nuke-mute heat waves, killing all the passengers of the 7.30 a.m. train leaving the Hoop Estates, destination Central London.

You told your sister to wear the long hiqabs you had stolen from the neighbours' clothesline. You told your sister to put on your air-purifying masks equipped with UV-protection visors. It was summer and the small declination of the earth's orbit meant the sun would come out earlier than it used to years ago. That, or the freakin' heat created by all the gases in the atmosphere and the fires in the Amazon. High-grade UV protection was obligatory outside the dome. It also made it impossible for the face-recognition software installed in all CCTV cameras and iris's readers at the entrance of the tube station to do their job.

This time you were going out.

You were a full two minutes behind schedule. The outside concourse of the Hoopway was already jam-packed with commuters trying to catch the 4:35 a.m. train, fully intent on making it in time for their first shift at newslavery. A lot of them were Colombian cleaners, like your abuela. Invisible, like your abuela. An army of immigrants which, if armed, could decide the course of the current political crisis. Turning it from constitutional crisis into fully-fledged civil war. An army tasked with making sure that all the shit pots in all the offices of Central London, the City and Canary Wharf were pristine, looking like a parallel universe of metal and glass well-paved highways and skyways, safe bridges, boutique charter schools, fast-lane airport terminals, flying cars and deluxe subways. The finance people would begin their ascent to their privatised crystal heavens later in the morning.

You knew some of the cleaners, some were your friends, you understood them, and they liked you because you would dare speaking a little Spanish to them in spite of the fact that it had been forbidden by PM de Pfeffel. They were allowed to remain in London after the purges; years after all the other communities were pushed to leave.

Many didn't stay, heading back home were things had been improving for over three decades now, or going to the U.S. after thirty-five out of the fifty-one states of the Union opened up their borders following the Tucson Armistice & Ceasefire. But some remained, perhaps out of loyalty to the generations that had arrived before them or because of the promise of full citizenship made by the government on condition of completing one thousand eight hundred and twenty-five days of voluntary work for free. Or else, it was the mere economic fact that Colombians and West Indians controlled most of the main routes of contraband in and out of the southern European war zone.

Your abuela's bloodline finally helped. You were a young woman with a plan. You talked to the Colombians, told them about your abuela, talked to them, sang with them, danced with them. You made your way in without attracting unwanted attention. You were their pet celebrity, their lil sista, la hermanita. The Colombians kept tabs on every movement in and out of the Domed Estates. They smuggled in food, cigarettes and alcohol, a luxury after the reinstitution of Prohibition and, of course, drugs. And they smuggled out weapons and provisions for the resistance in the south.

Their hard-won empire extended well beyond the Dome, the Hoopway, ex-London's Central City and the isles themselves. They opened or closed all the doors communicating the New Northern European Union with the war-torn south, operating out of Spain, the Canaries and West Africa. If you wanted to leave the isles undetected, you better ask the Colombians.

That was your plan. Get out of the Estate and into the Hoopway before the 4:35 a.m. train left for Central London. Reach the northwest quadrant before it gets sealed off, and hop on to the DLR at 5:17 a.m. That should give you plenty of time to reach Docklands at about six. Your Colombian friend would be waiting there. He had agreed to smuggle you and your sister into one of those DIY fiberglass submarines heading for Spain. From there you could decide whether to make your own way back to your relatives in South America, or whether to stay put. You had decided to leave everything behind and persuaded your sister to finally escape the nightmare.

This time you were going out.

Out on a shopping expedition.

But you did not count with two things: the sea of fire and an unscheduled Neet-Ceet Riot. The New Century Riots had become a sort of yearly tradition since at least 2021, commemorating the Second London riots, the suspension of the Olympic Games and the Greek Uprising. It is said the whole thing started with the self-immolation of the entire Greek team live on TV during the Games' inauguration of the games. Others argue the story is fake. The collective suicide never happened. Rather, it was the rebellion in Greece and Cyprus that quickly spilled over into Turkey, Italy, Spain, Southern France, North Africa, the Arab peninsula and the Occupied Territories. The Other Spring, they called it. In a matter of weeks, NATO did its best to crush the uprising. Their bombers set Athens ablaze and a myriad of underground groups retaliated in Central and Northern Europe. What was left of the EU was finally dissolved to be reborn under the aegis of Germany and Northern France as NEU, the New European Union. Without Britain, of course. The south exploded. England declared martial law. The Republic of Scotland declared itself neutral. The rest is history repeated.

24 His-Story

They say history repeats itself.

      But history is only his-story,

      and you haven't told us your story yet.

      In your story,

          names distinguish unlikely images from what is true.

      They help the dreamer forcing herself awake

      and to determine she is truly awake.

      To wake up from the nightmares and dreams of their
parents.

ANTROPOESIA
ANTROPOES
ANTROPOE
ANTRO
POE
SUN
RA

25   Vast of Night

The paintings of mental patients and those about to die.

They reveal something important about the relationship between words and images in the conventional perspective we've named reality.

It is no more than "a largely artificial construct which serves the limited ambitions of our central nervous systems," as the novelist say.

Consider reality.

The vast space of a recently discovered alien planet, in the process of being colonised.

The perimeter around your off-world station demarcated by an array of buffers, a system of watchtowers and laser-defences ready to supress affects and perceptions that may confuse or unsettle the sovereignty of your nervous system.

And yet, every now and then a clever thief bypasses the buffers, confounds the guards in the watchtowers and overcomes the laser-defences. Your dolls, Bowie. A magical object like a Tlingit coffin, a Narwa stone, a water whirlpool, a Kofan vortex-like object or the faces of fire demons in an ancient grimoire drawn and redrawn in a series of loosely defined sketches that are in fact no more than the shadowy outline of their original models.

Your mother used to draw such sketches during episodes of complete mental dissociation.

In her drawings, the souls of people would become vast landscapes in which wars were fought without end, never lost and never won.

You covered with them the walls of your bedroom walls.

Others found them disturbing, a set of arbitrarily

connected pictures and objects.

A spectrogram of planet earth coming off its hinges.

The suicide of the Greek Olympic team live on television.

Photos and drawings of the M5 during rush hour.

The contestants in the Great British Bake Off.

A front elevation of the balcony units of the British Embassy in Tehran after the nuclear explosion.

Transversal section of a goat with two heads from the West Coast of England.

Black and red sketches of the demons Nebiros and Ahriman, Tlingit coffins, Narwa stones, Kofan vortex-like objects.

A reproduction of Sartre's Hell Is Other People circa 1967.

Cut ups from the Sun Times showing a group of Neet kids throwing a petrol-meth bomb to riot policemen while holding a banner with the slogan 'Let's Riot' printed in Gothic font letters.

A scene from the Divine Comedy in which the poet and his daemon enter the gates of hell.

A reproduction of a painting from El Greco in the National Gallery of London showing King Phillip II of Spain in the act of kneeling down to pray while the gates of hell open up behind him like the giant jaws of an immense jaguar. Gardens devoured by a grotesque vegetation that springs from the debris of abandoned armoured cars and fallen airplanes somewhere near the port of Piraeus in Greece.

You in Disneyland holding on to somebody's hand (the person has been cut off from the photograph).

You would spend hours watching your mother while she was painting and making collages with old photographs. She would place the cut ups, tubes and water colours in perfect symmetrical order on top of the dining table. As the thirty-three cups with water and paint paste were set out on the large enamelled surface of the table, she would stare at them. Then, she would take four or five of them, combine the colours, the water and the paint dissolvent in a tea mug and heat it up inside the microwave oven. She would wait, standing up in front of the oven as the clock finished its strict thirty-three seconds countdown. The bell ringed. Opening the door, she would retrieve the mug and stare at the bobbing liquid. Then, stepping forward, she would carefully invert the brimming cup over her arms and her breasts. The hot liquid dripping over her white gown to form vortex-like coloured patterns. Like blossoming flowers.

You would stand there, looking at her. Contemplating the scene.

A shipwreck with spectator.

You found the scene quite moving, and the resulting canvas strangely beautiful. It would address you, call your name.

Invariably, your sister would interrupt the scene adding a bit of drama. She would run up to her shouting "why have you done that, mother?"

She would reply pointing at you with her index finger.

"The angel told me to."

26 Hot Liquid Artistic Collaboration

What compelled this artistic collaboration between your mother and you? I would like to think it was a sense of the intolerable.

The contrast between the plasticity of the hot liquid dripping through her body and the hardness of the curved topography formed by her elegant neck, her shoulders and her breasts.

As her porcelain skin got scolded, vapour rising from her extended arms, you burned inside.

You had never felt anything quite like it before.

The sheer realization that these opposites could be resolved in such a simple and elegant manner.

27   Drawings

One of the drawings on your bedroom wall depicted the people looking up to the heavens, asking for help.

An angel comes down, death from above, wearing a white gown decorated with psychedelic coloured flowers.

In her right hand she held a sword of fire.

She would have liked to stay and help, but a most violent gust is flowing from paradise.

Her golden wings trapped in the swirl she is propelled forwards, her face turned towards the people. She sees the ground cracking beneath the peoples' feet and the gates of hell opening up, swallowing them as if the earth itself had turned into a jaguar, a bug predator or a devouring vegetation that had sprung from the debris of abandoned armoured cars and fallen airplanes.

Your sister looked at you with a mixture of pity and fear.

Where are we? What happened?

You asked.

We got caught in an unscheduled riot, your sister said. Some Marilyn Monroe-shifter hit you on the head with a zenade. You went nuts, almost ripped her apart while drifting in and out of consciousness. I dragged you up this side of the Hoopway and took a tube updraft. Nothing to worry about. We made it just in time to take the 4:35 a.m. train. You were out of mind, seeing colours and blossomed flowery paintings, singing Baby Gaga songs. Yet you moved swiftly, as if sleepwalking. Do you sleepwalk? No problem with the iris-recon. UV goggles worked a treat. But if we want to be at Docklands by six we're going to have to come up with some mammoth Plan B.

What's the plan? You asked her. Don't know, she said, but I'll tell you as soon as I've got one.

Just working on it, your sister said.

She figured there would be a long queue at the Infinite Divisibility Checkpoint. She could use her charms to woe one or two of the security guards manning the checkpoint.

Her dumbass boyfriend referred to her perfectly rounded buttocks as a perfect illustration of the constant curve of the falling declination of the earth. That's why he called her Doomsday Girl.

Her charms worked a treat. Oscar-deserving performance. Long eyelashes, hands, plunging neckline, skin-tight catsuit, the contours of her figure becoming the curvilinear equivalent of the checkpoint's sandbags, the chairs and the electronic screens of the checkpoint. It took her five minutes to distract the two young security guards. Long enough to allow you safe passage. She signalled you to keep going. As you made your way towards the mag lev, you turned back and saw their bodies becoming the curved lines of the screens, the walls, the infinite divisibility of the cosmic treadmills and the ceilings.

Your sister was multiplying herself into the time and space of the Infinite Divisibility Checkpoint.

You became acutely aware of the fact that the limbs, heads, skin and musculature of the people waiting in line to board the DLR mag lev were not part of any meaningful unity, like a group or an individual human body. Instead, they persisted on their own floating in the bitterly cold air of the Thames estuary in January. You saw severed pairs of Katie Price's breasts, Marilyn Monroe lookalike faces mashed up with the features of Baby Gaga and the detached, surgically enhanced lips of an eternal Lana Del Rey together with the coiffed hairdo of James Dean retro-imitators.

They all formed the perfectly ordered queue of people waiting to board the train.

Your sister was late. You doubted whether to go back to the Checkpoint or take your place in the line of people waiting for the train. She told you to keep going, come what may. That's what you should do. She knows your Colombian friend will be waiting by the entrance to Docklands Pier.

She'll make it.

Don't be nervous.

To calm yourself you unwrapped a falsemeat doughnut and kept eating until the maglev stopped in front of the platform. You stood up, threw the rest of the falsemeat in the bin nearby and went in. You sat down all back of the bus, waiting for your sister to show up at the last minute.

She didn't.

Mind the gap,
said the disembodied voice.

All back of the bus.

She didn't make it.

Other People

Hell is other people. Jean-Paul Sartre. No Exit, 1966.

Fully flexible philosophical action-figure. Collectors' item. Authorised use of the name by the Weyland-Incorporated French Republic. Ten per cent of the profits will go to support the Resistance fighting against the new Reich in the southern front. Do your part. Down with retro-fascist capitalism!

Action-figures of radical philosophers were the latest retro-craze to come out of France. The huge billboard advert was visible from the porthole of the fiberglass submersible approaching the port of Calais. They came in human-size boxes wrapped in transparent paper. Fully robotised, capable of delivering wise philosophemes out of the most complete data bases of the history of ideas available at the push of a button. On voice command, they could answer complex existential or metaphysical questions and provide self-help advice. You could also download their apps into your implanted smart phone, wisdom for a few pound-credits.

All-action rad philosophers were, in all aspects of detail, fully human. They were perfect seventh generation androids: tall, mobile, conversant, emotional. You had never seen them with your own eyes until the day when you and your sister won a shopping expedition to ex-London Central City in a wireless TV program. You stopped in front of the windows at Selfridge's a few days before Three Christmases, and there they were: Karl Marx, Sigmund Freud, and Friedrich Nietzsche in retro-hipster gear at the centre of the window's holiday arrangement. Each figure had a soundbite, depicted as one of those bubble-like vignettes used in old-fashioned comic books. It read: buy us, we're the Masters of Suspicion! To the left, Anacharsis the Scythian, Ernesto "Che" Guevara and your all-time cult favourite Slavoj Žižek.

Caption: Do you think your righteousness will pay back your debt? I doubt it. Support the revolution!

You were particularly impressed by the Žižek figure. It looked the piece. Dishevelled, unkempt, its grey t-shirt covered in sweat and Coca-Cola stains. The window was interactive. Your sister pressed the key on the window screen and Slavoj walked towards you. Fixing his blue eyes on yours, the android shouted: Fuck you! A spray of sweat and saliva covered the window. It was the coolest thing you had seen in a very long time. I get him sis. You said. I would pay to get told off like that.

If only we had the Universal Army.

Your sis. Where was she? You were about to dock at the port of Calais, the rad philosophers' billboard greeting you from the boardwalk. No time to get out of the sub-boat, said your Colombian friend. We're only here to pick up cargo. That's all. Something important, they say. It better be, you said. I don't like stopping in Inco-France. You never know who's inco and who's rebel; you never know with these frog bastards. Are you hungry? I thought it was going to be two of you. What happened to your pretty sister? Está buena, right?

In case you got separated, she had said, you would continue on your own and meet exactly one year from now in a bar called Cronos Devorando a Sus Hijos in downtown post-Madrid.

You kept going.

You were at sea.

You got out.

Your Colombian friend and the other two members of the sub-boat crew returned with food and a sizeable wooden crate gliding on top of floaters. Make way, said the only woman among them. She must have been about your sister's age or a little older. You thought she was pretty. In a Katy

Perry-tribute kind of way. She had blue hair, heavy retro-1950s make up, a Visit LA tank top, bright blue Plastic Ono leggings and smelled of strawberries. Alas, she was armed to the teeth. Blades, sputchsticks, anti-male pheromones, various glowing implants under her skin, and the biggest hi-freq unweapon you had ever seen. She called it her Little Bastard.

The name? Me llamo Clara Pontes, she said. But the guys call me Clara Pandy. You're cute. You can call me whatever you want. Y tú? What's your name? My name is Hoodoo Girl, you replied. No surname. No name. Just Hoodoo Girl. Ok, Just Hoodoo Girl, where are you going? I don´t know. Out, you said. Out where? asked Clara Pandy. Just out, you responded. Clara laughed. I like it, she said. A girl with a plan.

I wanted out, that's all, you interrupted. My sister and I got separated at Docklands. I'm meeting her later on at a bar called Cronos Devorando a Sus Hijos in post-Madrid.

I know the place, Clara said. An exo girl like you wouldn't last a minute there. It's full of men and they're all bastards. I see you speak Lat-Spanish, but you don't look like your friend; stick with me and I'll help you out, I'll take you there. Don't trust your friend, criminals the lot of them, sudacas de mierda.

What's a sudaca? You asked. Are they supposed to look like something else?

Shut up bitch, cierra el pico. You don't listen to her, said your Colombian friend putting an abrupt end to the conversation upon entering the cargo bay. Behind him was the big wooden crate on floaties. She's done too much crystal coke and her brain has turned into tortilla española, chapetona bitch. Yeah, I'm sure you'll better off with this gilipollas impotente, replied Clara. She exchanged a smile with you on her way out. Winked an eye. Hablamos luego, she said. It's good to have someone on board with whom I can make intelligent conversation, for a change, she said. As she left the bay, she put her left hand in her underwear and gave your friend the finger. You smiled back at her.

I love her, said your Colombian friend. She's batshit crazy but would take a bullet for you any minute. Oh, and she's into girls, in case you wanna know. I have to tell PA that you're going work in this boat. Otherwise, he'll throw you out. What's it gonna be? Can you cook? Yes, I can cook, you said. My sister can't and my mother never did, so I was always in charge. That's settled then, said your Colombian friend. I'll go to the bridge and tell PA. You wait here.

Who's PA? you asked. He's the steerman, sort of the Captain I suppose. He's Danish, un vikingo cachondo. I'll introduce you later. He's still pissed because I didn't tell him I was bringing you on board. No one knows his real name but we call him PA because of his favourite character, a boy in some Danish novel who quits school one morning and decides to live up a tree. He told us the story once. From that tree, PA reveals to his friends the truth: that nothing matters and it's no point doing anything. Cool stuff. The sort of thing you would expect from the Danes. Don't you think? The rest of the crew are pretty simple. Clara, you met her already. She's our woman-at-arms and fucking good at it. Takes no shit from no one, specially dudes. We're always insulting each other, but that's just because we like each other. Then there's me. I fix things. I'm the mechanic around here, and sort of the negotiator. A diplomat. The go-between Clara and PA. I have to be because they're always at each other's throats. A thousand years ago they had history together. PA cannot take she's no longer interested. Me? I don't care. A girlfriend and a boyfriend in every port. I'm a sailor like my father. Like his father and his father's father. He was born here but his parents were illegals from Colombia. He had navy experience, so he joined the fight when things went bunkers here, to get citizenship. I guess it mattered in those days. Now I couldn't give two shits about it. I burnt my military service card after what they did during the riots in Guernica. Went awol. Have been ever since. I mean, they rounded all these kids, friends of mine from school and shit, said they were anarchists and muslims and ordered us to shoot them. Put them down like dogs. I shot the Sarge instead. So, you can cook? Good then. It's settled. Sleep now. You'll have plenty of work tomorrow. One last thing. See that crate? Don't touch it. Not in a million years. No matter what. Don't touch it. You've been warned, said your Colombian friend.

What's in it? You asked.

None of your business, he replied.

But they say our lives may depend on it.

30 The Crate

What's in the crate?

    You loved inventory lists.

    You Queen.

    You collector.

    Here's one:

    (a) a kilobillion in gold credit-pounds;

    (b) the ultimate unweapon en route to the rebels in Greece;

    (c) the disassembled body of an eight-generation drone warrior by Weyland Incorporated;

    (d) key intelligence for sale to the biggest buyer;

    (e) key artificial intelligence for sale to the biggest buyer;

    (f) the terms of an armistice;

    (g) drugs, lots of drugs;

    (h) a philosopher action-figure with the answer to all riddles;

    (i) a kaiju monster;

    (j) the fly that just passed by you;

    (k) nothing, like in the movies.

    You fell asleep making lists in your mind, and didn't notice the storm that broke out in the Channel. The sub was rocked by a must violent gust, which sent it forwards into the unknown. Looking backwards, you sleepwalked. It hadn't happened in a very long time. You moved along the corridors, opened hatches and held on to handles when the boat went from one side to the other.

    But you didn't wake up.

    The boat seemed huge, endless and labyrinthine, as if it were suspended in forever time and always space. The void a vanishing point. The non-place that haunts every place. In the no-place that haunts every place.

Though in deep sleep, in dream time you became fully conscious of the fact that you were able to name things: this is a sub, I am sleep, there is a storm out there, this is the cargo bay, that is a tool in my hand, here is the wooden crate.

You used the tool to force open the wooden crate. What you saw in there made you lose your grip and the tool fell very, very slowly. Time was about to begin moving backwards when the tool hit the floor of the cargo bay and made almost as much noise as the bells of Westminster cathedral. A tool is never just a tool. You covered your ears and watched the lid of the crate fall back into its original position. The noise and the glimmer that had blinded you stopped.

Time began moving forwards once again and you woke up. At first, you doubted yourself: the dreamer cannot know the difference between being asleep or awake. Looking around you, you noticed that the reaches of the cargo bay no longer were those of proper space. This is forever time and always space, you said to yourself. I am in the no-place that haunts every place. The tool, the unweapons, the contraband and the wooden crate lured each other, and you, in a fascinating embrace.

A simulation inviting the sensual gathering of all things without penetrating them, letting them be.

This is me, that is the cargo bay, you said. But it has no discernible end. It has become the scene of a battle between that which appears and whatever it is that we cannot see. Am I one with all these things in always space? Or is our gathering a chance encounter between the storm out there and my sleepwalking in here? I am awake, and yet, it's all just a free association, like the lists I make, vicarious connections and relations necessarily contingent.

Chance determinant.

The others must have heard the noise. It was deafening. They must be on their way here, weapons at the ready. If they find me here, they will conclude I opened the crate. Perhaps they will abandon me in the next port, blast me into micro-molecules of plasma, bits one and zero or sell my mirrorsoul to a neoslaver. They can throw me overboard and I'll become bait for giant mutated squids and abyssal fish.

Better to move. Better to get out of here.

Come on sleepwalking girl!

Back to bed, back to making lists:

a map to Uqbar;

a letter by Gunnar Erfjord dated March 1941;

several hrönir;

the mashed-up face of Baroness Elsa von Loringhoven and Vincenz Grimm;

the aleph;

nothing,

like in the movies.

The storm moved things around in the cargo bay. It must have cracked open the wooden crate. Something moved in there. Didn't it? You saw it. Then again, you are sleepwalking.

Aren't you, silly girl?

31 Horrorscope

Your mother liked it when you read the horoscope to her out loud. It was full of clichés about Venus appearing before the Sun in the house of Capricorn. A new love around the corner, money, fame, fortune and red candles. There was nothing in them about freak storms, sleepwalking or monsters. It was all quite simple, safe, uninteresting.

You began making your own astrological charts, inserting stranger things and peculiar goings on. Finding meaning among indifferent stars. The ancients called it mathesis, the learning. It was preeminent among all kinds of knowledge. But only those who had been touched by the gods would be able to understand the language of hidden signs, and to interpret for others the significance of a new light or sudden darkness in the skies. It was clear for the ancients, as it became clear for you, that failure to heed the signs would lead to disaster.

Most ordinary people look for sufficient reason, a masterplan or a supreme architect whose secret intentions explain all accidents. They disavow the learning and merely kid themselves. You understood very quickly that the point was not to deliver instructions or sell recipes. Rather, since the planets and the stars couldn't care less about the fate of puny little humans, the fact is that it is always up to us. Failure to heed the signs would lead to disaster.

What you saw that night in the cargo bay was a sign, something fallen from the heavens, the object of an astrological chart.

Charts are based on the idea that events cast shadows before them. That is, before they come to take place. Nevertheless, they remain unnoticed. Like shadows, or the messiah.

Mysteries.

Signs do not tell you what to do in the face of doom. They stand for something else at once simpler and far more terrible: that no matter when the end of days happens, the problem with the apocalypse is that it is never apocalyptic enough.

You must always build with whatever is left from the wreckage.

Sitting alone on the deck of the sub boat you looked up to the planet and the stars, marvelling at their muteness and indifference. The others were worried. Their boat had been thrown off course by the freak storm that began the night you sleepwalked and lasted about a week. By now, they had no idea about their current position. These fiberglass subs had no real navigation equipment, only a crude GPS salvaged from a few old smartphones.

Alas, this was no real crew. Just a ragtag bunch of jobless assholes with little or no experience in the high seas. They coasted but did not navigate. It would take ages before they could retrace their steps and go back to the continent. Not to say anything about inspection drones and damn inquisitor eurosubs.

PA was mad at you. The contraband would go to ruin and they wouldn't get paid. Whatever it was hidden in that wooden crate, they had been offered good money to take it down south in time. Some people are going to get very angry, said PA. And it's all you fault little girl. I knew you coming on board was a bad omen. She's a witch, he said to the others. I've seen her wandering around the corridors like a soulless corpse. We should get rid of her as soon as we touch land anywhere.

Clara came to your help. Grabbing PA by the balls, she pushed him against the fiberglass panels of the sub. Calm down, she said to him, putting a blade against his throat.

Stop it, the two of you! Shouted your Colombian friend while charging the unweapon in his hands. We can still make it, he said. The girl knows the stars. I've seen her reading the skies, he said. She can take us back. PA decided to let it go, for now. Clara put one of her sputchsticks in your hands. From now on you carry this one. Always. And you better grow eyes on that cute little ass of yours!

She said.

That's how you ended up on the deck all night long, looking at the planets and the constellations. Them little lights. Freezing in the cold air of the north Atlantic. Searching for signs among the stars.

Failure to read the signs would lead to disaster. But if you were to read them properly, ripples in the tide, changes in the colour of atmospheric gases, strange wind patterns, Seneca guns or fallen asteroids, whatever they threw at you, perhaps things would occur without loss of much life.

That night the monster appeared out of nowhere. It was not meant to be seen. It was not destined for you, but you had voyaged too far. So it happened, suddenly, unexpectedly and in the half-light of-glimpses. You caught sight of another visible order intersecting with ours.

At a speed of twenty-five frames per second.

In that disconcerting moment, you saw between frames.

And it looked back at you with its dark empty eye as it travelled alongside the boat, same speed but double its size.

Did the white demon now beside you fell from the sky into the black water?

Is it one or many?

In the story your abuela told you many times during nights like this, Jesus of Nazareth travels from Galilee to the Gerasene and is met by local villagers who beg him to cure one of their elders who has been possessed by demons. The old man roamed naked among the ruins of a cemetery, setting things on fire, cutting himself, crying and screaming alone at night.

Finally, Jesus heeds to the villagers' appeal and reluctantly confronts the old man in a half-destroyed mausoleum. Jesus is afraid. Making sure no one notices, he collects pieces of rock and hides them within his tunic, ready to smash the head of the old man if he goes in a frenzy. After all, hell is other people.

Jesus steps forward and asks the man, what is your name? The old man replies: my name is Legion, for we are many. Then, Jesus casts the demons out of the body of the old man and commands them to take possession of a herd of swine in a nearby hill. The swine attack Jesus, biting and disfiguring him. Hurt, angry and mad, Jesus compels them to rush over the side of a cliff and into the sea below. Then he stones the old man and throws his corpse off the cliff.

Having witnessed the whole scene, the terrified villagers urge Jesus and his followers to leave.

Who was the monster of the story? The old man? The swine? The demons? Was it Jesus himself whose awesome demonstrations of power instilled untold horror into the hearts of the villagers? They banned him from entering their village ever again.

The question imposed itself with full force: is the beast beside you a demon fallen from the sky just as the swine fell from a cliff?

Or has it seen something inside you and recognised you as one of their kin?

You wanted out.

Now you were voyaging far.

Into the night of the world.

In the light between frames.

Lost in the sea of names and words.

Like the beast in the story, this one has a multitude of

names, a series that cannot support itself since the name is arbitrary and has no intrinsic relation to anything else. I is many, the space of all names grasping itself as force. Now you grasp yourself as having the power of the sea-beast whose name you have invented and bestowed upon. Like Jesus, when he asked the multitude of demons to give their name. In that moment he gained universal power over them and could destroy them.

That night, after the encounter with the sea-demon, you went to bed knowing yourself free and powerful.

You had understanding of the world and its creatures.

Now, you were ready to fulfil your quest.

You went to bed thinking of yourself as Jesus, demon slayer.

The mass of the indecisive.

Waves of lustful bodies falling like starlings in winter. Like a black wind, or a tempest. A swarm of the living dead devouring each other. A sea of boiling blood and drowning bodies. The forest of the suicidal. A barren desert of open graves. An inverted pyramid of empty coffins. A seemingly infinite field of women, children and men ridden with leprosy. You at the gates of the city of Dis.

My name is Legion. Speak to me of horror.

33   Notes on the City of Monsters

Those who take a downward turn. The victims of disaster. Those who were here when the killing fields opened their jaws and swallowed us whole. When the fragile skies came crumbling down. Them, enveloped in a downward continuum become marked beings. Monsters.

(Where she wrote "monsters", he corrected, crossing over her word in the style used back in the century to save paper, and wrote "beings").

Whoever comes out wounded from a catastrophic event or from a life of suffering prompts the question: Is she part, or the cause, of our current predicament?

(You have asked this yourself many times, am I the sign of an impending apocalypse?)

By coming upon the scene as the carrier of a message, a harbinger of the end of days, the custodian becomes the very embodiment of that which is announced. And hence, a monstrous being.

Gordon & Gordon say: "take the notion of a divine warning seriously, and, in doing so, take the victim, the survivor, who could also be a victim by virtue of the memory and scars carried, or the witness of disaster, to be a kind of monster."

Such is the first path into the city.

Monstrum, from the Latin verb monere, meant to deliver a message. To warn or admonish. Warnings always come from above, where stars and planets share the non-place, the always space and forever time with gods, demigods, and demons who were many times thought of as stars and planets themselves.

Seen from space the earth itself becomes a message.

This has been proven by the testimonies of cosmonauts

and spacewalkers in which the word 'fragile' is repeated as a warning time and time again. But we don't listen. Seen from space, the earth itself becomes monstrous, a strange attractor. This has been demonstrated by the fact that those who have walked in space and contemplated it from afar immediately wish to kill themselves, to become one with the immense vacuum of outer space or fall off a cliff, so to speak.

They invariably lose their minds after the event.

Edward White floated in space for twenty minutes. Noticing that looked at from a hundred and twenty miles away the earth seemed featureless, he refused to come back to the space capsule that kept him alive. Two years after his space walk, he died in a freak fire at Cape Canaveral. A few years later, his wife took her own life.

Russian cosmonaut Alexei Leonov left Voskohod 2 jumping head on into the eternal black sea of outer space. He remained there a mere ten minutes. But he too refused to come back. Others who did come back, like Michael Collins, have consistently refused to talk about what they saw.

(What did they see? Or was something they impossibly heard in the vacuum of space, an incomprehensible voice perhaps?).

We comfort ourselves in the thought that our planet is a cradle of life, a benign being. What if we are wrong? What if the solitary traveller in the vast indifferent sea is, in fact, the monster?

Perhaps the reason why astronauts, cosmonauts and other spacewalkers did not wish to come back or say a word about it is because the planet reclaimed them. Like a jealous mother who would go to any length to stop her daughter from leaving her side, even denouncing her before the authorities as a foreign terrorist or an alien invader.

Or a witch, learned in astrology and black arts.

But we knew this already.

According to Hesiod, the monstrous Cyclops were the primordial sons of the earth and the sky. Brontes the Thunderer, Steropes the Bearer of Lightning, and Arges the Bright had a single eye in the middle of their foreheads. They smelled of faeces and urine and were gigantic. The Cyclops were incredibly strong, stubborn, and hostile. Their desire was to arm the sons and daughters of the Titans and watch them crush one another. To this purpose they fashioned the first unweapons: lightning bolt for Zeus, a trident for Poseidon, bow and arrows for Artemis Cthonic and sunbright Apollo, and a helmet of darkness for Hades. They forged these somethings out of nothingness. These were the first and most lethal of all negativity weapons.

Jorge Luis Borges recalls somewhere that "before it became the name of an optical instrument, the word 'monocle' was applied to beings who had a single eye."

Like a shining beacon in the sky.

He cited Góngora's *Monóculo Galán de Galatea*: "Un monte era de miembros eminente / Este que, de Neptuno hijo fiero / de un ojo ilustra el orbe de su frente / Émulo casi del mayor lucero."

[*An eminent peak of limbs he was, this uncouth son of Neptune, lighting the orb of his forehead with an eye almost rivalling the greatest star.*]

According to the Argentinean poet these lines outdo and are weaker than those of Virgil, which in turn outdo and are weaker that other lines from the Odyssey, all of them weaker still than those of Hesiod.

His poetry closes the circle.

The second path into the city of monsters is to acknowledge them as the harbingers of things we ourselves would not like to know or face. If so, Borges's notion that the decline of the power of monsters matches a decline in our belief in them turns out to be monstrous itself.

For it would mean that we have blinded ourselves.

(Not even one-eyed, like the Cyclops).

We fear these harbingers will bring catastrophes upon us by appearing to us. We blame such victims thinking that we can avoid disaster by marking them. But in doing so, we bring catastrophe upon ourselves.

Richard Cavendish wrote in *A History of Magic* that "a person's physical peculiarities, mannerisms of speech and walk, the colour of her eyes or skin, the shape of her nails and the position of moles in her body, were regarded as indications of her fate and character."

Remember the mole in the back of your arm and the bump in your head, little girl? Aged eleven you began noticing that you would feel dizzy when you touched it. Gave you headaches. At other times visions.

Scared, your mother refused to take you to the doctor and appealed instead to the priest in the Autofaith-sanctioned parish church. The priest, a man in his late fifties paid you a visit after your abuela had passed away. He asked to be left alone with you. He looked at the bump on your head, and the oval-shaped mole on the back of your forearm. He considered the number and disposition of your toes and toenails, and examined your tongue and your teeth, and then your thighs and the orifices between your thighs searching for teeth in them. He whispered things in your ears, words, phrases you could not understand but which became deeply seated in your mind.

Many years later, while searching the contents of the cargo bay in the sub, you found out where those words came from. You stumbled upon them while browsing the pages of Heinrich Kramer and Jacob Sprenger's *Malleus Maleficarum*, published in fourteen hundred and eighty-six. The book is also known as *The Hammer of Witches*. In Part Three, you read for the first time the words that came to your head every time you felt dizzy or became overwhelmed by headaches and visions.

The book described such happenings as the consequence of contagion or commerce with a demon. It referred to three kinds of communication with air spirits.

The first one, with a presence made out of night and smokeless fire or air, which affects the body of the person possessed. It would manifest in manifold ways, from dizziness and headaches, to sleepwalking and narcolepsy. And in adult males and females as extreme sexual desire followed by melancholia.

In the second, the spirit connection would manifest itself as a change in the relation between the body of the person and the surrounding environment. As plague or aerial miasma, of the kind described in Mary Shelley's *The Last Man*. The plague may end up turning all but a handful of human beings into zombies, in the manner made popular by B-movies, TV series and in the short stories of Roberto Bolaño. It could lead to mass hysteria and mob behaviour, as in Neet Riots or revolutionary fervour, which were all thought during the Old and New Dark Ages as the result of the action of devils.

Finally, a third kind of communication. This one much more abstract and metaphysical. In it the demon possesses not the living and the animate but the inorganic and the inanimate. This is the kind of communication behind sudden changes in the weather, the appearance of freak storms, outbursts of geological activity or long periods of steady climate change and the stresses and strains of rising and falling sea levels. This kind of interaction ends with the pent-up rage of the earth itself being released, as in earthquakes, pandemics and cataclysms.

The latter is the one that comes closest to a description of the planet as monstrous. Similar to the testimonies of astronauts and cosmonauts and all manner of spacewalkers. You learned it was no coincidence that twenty-first century geologist Bill McGuire had called his definitive treatise on the relation between climate fluctuations and the increase on the geological activity of the planet, *Waking the Giant*.

Others had observed in times past the possibility that the planet might be an entity separated from the world as it appears to us, something alien and indifferent to the fate of humans. They were the first among us to give such realization a monstrous and demonic form.

35 The Jinn

In accordance with the Muslim tradition, Allah created something other than angels and humans.

He also created the Jinn.

Angels were made of light.

Humans were made out of mud.

But the Jinn were made of black smokeless fire or the black cold water of the far away ice seas, which also burns the skin.

They were made thousands of years before the first man walked the earth. Hundreds of thousands before the first man walked into outer space.

Al Qaswini says, "the Jinn are aerial animals with transparent bodies, which can assume a variety of forms." Borges adds that "they may show themselves as clouds or as huge undefined pillars; but when their form becomes condensed, they become visible, perhaps in the bulk of a man."[1]

He cited English orientalist Edward Lane, who writes that "when the Jinn take the shape of animals or human beings they are sometimes of an enormously gigantic size; they are also said to become invisible at pleasure by a rapid extension or rarefaction of the particles which compose them, when they may disappear into the air or earth or through a solid wall."

Crucially, for both the Arabs and the Egyptians "the pillarlike whirlwinds of sand raised in the desert are caused by the flight of an evil Jinnee." In saying this they observe no superstition. Rather, not only they refer to the fact that

---

[1] Credit to JL Borges, *The Book of Imaginary Beings* (Vintage, 2002) 84-86. He cites Al Qaswini.

some terrane and subterranean events are intimately linked to those above the ground, like sand and sea storms, violent gusts, or winds seemingly coming out of nowhere. But also attend to something much more significant about the nature of disasters.

This is the fact that in the Moslem tradition the Apocalypse is not some moment when history is abolished and in accordance to the accumulated weight of our good and evil deeds, we arrive at some or other destination. Instead, following a much older Egyptian tradition, Apocalypse, for the Moslem, is not a when, but rather, the event that attests to the immensity of the ultimate act of giving.

This means that time and everything that exists of it and within it cannot stop, defer or foreclose it because such is the gift of Allah. It can neither be appropriated nor exhausted by human want or desire. Time, the time of the cosmos, the stars, and the planets, is a variation of the infinite, the inaccessible and the unknown. In the infinity of time we humans confront a cosmos that is profoundly unhuman, unresponsive to will, our wishes or needy desires. Here, we come to realize that there is a level of reality and possibility. Another path, exemplified by the planet as such when looked at from outer space, which is truly hidden from us, impervious to assimilation by either religion or science.

Horror is the affect that accompanies such realization; it is embodied in the Jinn and expressed in their ambiguous nature.

Reading books such as the ones mentioned above you learned that there are good Jinn and evil Jinn, male Jinn and female Jinn, false believers and true unbelievers, visible and invisible Jinn.

There are Jinn who can attain the lower heavens "where they overhear the conversations of angels about future events," as Borges explains, and can be of much help to seers, witches and magi.

(You often listened to their talk, careful not to be noticed. At first, their voices sounded like shrieking noises, unintelligible to the human ear, like radio static or the music speed prog band The James Dean. Progressively, you began making sense of their chatter. That was around the time the front man of The James Dean committed suicide live on stage during a rendition of their hit The Forest.).

But they may also be lying, their lies just an analogy of the unknown but real future. They may grant you a wish, if you free them from whatever prison Allah the Merciful may have chosen for them. Often a bottle found at sea, in a cave, a well, a river, an uninhabited house, or a crossroads. But if you do ask to be granted a wish, they will hold you in their debt. An eternal and unpayable debt. The sort of cosmic debt that ghoul Jinn attempt to collect by feeding upon the dead. The word 'genius' has been associated with the name of these blue giants. That may well be an error, a misunderstanding or the result of idiomatic coincidence, for the Latin term *genius* means to beget or to bring into existence something out of nothing, as in the granting of a wish but also as in the term 'war begets more war' or 'money begets money.'

The latter are examples of infinity gone wrong; a time warp caught inside a loop. As in the monstrous idea that time will return in the self-same numerical order and that change is no more than a well-concocted and convenient human illusion. Such is the viewpoint embodied by many of the Jinn portrayed in recent literature, in the writings of Einstein and the Quineans. Or in the character fittingly named Dr. Manhattan, invented by Allan Moore. Gabriel García Márquez wrote "nothing ever happens in Macondo," and Julio Cortázar came up with the story of a man who listens to a telephone conversation in modern Paris while at the same time he witnesses the devastation of Ancient Rome by means of fire. In Tomás Eloy Martínez's *Purgatory*, Simón Cardoso, who has been dead for some thirty years, waits until the wheel of time completes its turn in order to re-enter our timeline in the lounge bar of Trudy Tuesday in New Jersey.

It is said that the circle of time is red, and that its entrance is concealed deep in hell. Some refer to it as the eternal noon, a landscape made of time where all past, the not-yet and the future exist together and the sun itself burns without intermission. Others call it this: The Garden.

The Garden appears only in a handful of grimoires, composed by the most obscure and wisest among the *palabreros* and the magi. Sometimes, it is depicted as a circumference touched by a tangent that extends off the edges of the page. *A fonds perdu*. The circle represents time constantly revolving, and the point of contact with the tangent is the unmoving present. Our gaze tends to focus on that which moves, but if for a moment we were to stop and fixate on the present, noon would be eternal.

This is why the creature in Mary Shelley's tale flees north. He is searching for the land of eternal noon.

He is looking for the entrance to The Garden.

Like the Jinn, the creature is also a being released from the normal constraints of time and matter, since he was put together out of source materials that had already died and thus overcome the boundary between the animate and the inanimate. He did not end, for if something ends it's not eternal.

It is really all a matter of maths and geometry.

The creature escaped along the tangent.

(Like you).

While the wheel of time kept moving, you went out.

Zeno explained: what moves does not move in the place in which it is or in the place in which it is not.

There's also a non-place that haunts every place.

36 The Creature

Mocked by everyone and everything around him, the creature fled to the Arctic.

There,

according to the story,

in a final act of sacrifice he set himself on fire.

"I shall collect my funeral pile, and consume to ashes this miserable frame, that its remains may afford no light to any curious and unhallowed wretch, who would create such another as I have been. Light, feeling, and sense will pass away."

But this is not what really happened.

Like you, he became an adept of books. Illuminated books where letters turn into animals and birds alight in those letters. Grimoires in which the riddle of time is posited but never answered. Those were his favourites. "Time shifts back and forth – sometimes I open my eyes onto old wooden houses, mica works, monasteries, fisheries, at other times the same land's deserted."[2]

Farther north he saw the Archangel Monastery's high walls. The walls of the monastery have seven gates, seven towers, seven labyrinths and seven black cannons embedded in their seven walls of stone. Over seven hundred monks live there, served by seven hundred peasants and artisans who survive off the peculiar crops that grow in the surrounding grounds.

Coca leaves.

---

[2] Credit to L Sheck, *A Monster's Notes* (Knopf, 2012) 21.

Munching on them.

Ayahuasca.

The purple flower that grows in lands where cadavers are abandoned, in the shadow of trees more ancient than the forest.

In the scriptorium, a young monk known only as John the Scott, drew in coloured ink fantastic birds, animals and flowers composed out of pieces of other birds, animals, and flowers. He was transcribing the teachings of the old *Book of the True Law*.

That winter he wanted to leave something beautiful behind.

Instead, when traders arrived into the monastery the next Spring, they found the land desolate, the blue-painted ceilings with their little gold stars peeled, badly faded, and no trace of the monks, the peasants, the artisans, or the servants.

Only ashes.

Some say something John had summoned obliterated everything.

It was, perhaps, the ever-consuming sun of an eternal noon.

"Something in me obliterates everything," said the creature as he travelled even farther north. His books didn't explain how time could shift back and forth, but in Lomonosov's first treatise on icebergs he found clues. "Words that contain the vowels e, i and u in their first syllable should be used to summon tender beings, while those with the vowel sounds o, u, and y must be avoided, since they are fit to describe things that cause fear."

(If it's true, as Aristotle said, that we're human only because we are born to language, then what are we? Are we tender beings, or things that cause fear? What are you, girl?).

Lomonosov wrote, "a cold fire envelops me; the icy oceans are burning."

He believed that although the present is fixed, persistent and stable, what dwells within it is not. Certain bodies are fluid, able to move in unison with the circle of time that is constantly revolving. Our gaze tends to concentrate on that which moves only in appearance within the fixed present, but if we were able to stop and contemplate it in the half-light-of-glimpses or in between frames, noon would be eternal.

"The scenery changes and the seasons pass, but the window that frames the scene is always the same," he said.

This is what really happened.

When it reached the farthest point in the Arctic, the creature didn't move. If it moved, time would move too. The creature understood that only life and the present were static. That even eternal noon comes to an end, "just as waiting does in purgatory," as the writer says. "You linger there for eternity, but on the far side of eternity is paradise."

On the far side is The Garden.

This is no self-sacrifice. Those in the know call it the Severance. It is a severing of the ties binding you to this world in the present, a breaking free from the shackles that have been steadily placed around you since birth by those closest to you. You, however, you were a fluid body. Already in the fringes, one step from being an outsider.

That night you stopped moving. If you moved, time would move too. Like Shelley's creature, like John the Scott and the Jinn of tradition, you crossed over.

You went out.

You escaped through the tangent; and have ever since remained motionless in the present looking backward and yet moving forward.

Where are you heading?

I don't know. To you everything was and is a return. You could play with dirt and excrement, with darkness, the night, and the hiddenness of the world, and it would be all right. You could return it to any situation that has become too pure and too orderly, "and thus sterile," as Stone says.[3]

You could die here and now, and it would be all right.

---

[3] Credit to S Stone, 'The Nightside Tarot', in *Diabolical* (Scarlet Imprint, 2009) 125.

37   Montaged Self

The creature wanted to shed its montaged self, made of parts sliced out of others.

Such is the third path into the garden.

The monstrous garden that both contains and sublates the previous two.

Monsters are lyrical essays, mirroring the world not as it appears to us but revealing only its hiddenness and darkness.

The monster isn't a slave marked by skin colour or a montaged body. In the past, these features of birth always proved insufficient. Enslaved people were branded in the United States. Jews, Gypsies, Communists, Blacks and homosexuals were rounded in concentration camps in Germany, together with Latinos and other others in post-Brexit Britain. Women and Moors were burnt in the stake during the autos da fé in Portugal, Spain and the Americas. Palestinians were starved and choked to death in the Occupied Territories. Greeks were pushed to commit mass suicide during the break-up of the Union. All of them were tattooed. In your present, the grammar of branding has been sustained by denying people access to language and grammar. No, the monster isn't a slave marked by skin colour.

She's a sequence.

Ready-Made World

In the first years of the twenty-first century, one of the southern states of the Union banned brown people from reading William Shakespeare's *The Tempest* and Mary Shelley's *Frankenstein*.

Not being allowed access to books, they began telling their stories to one another and to others. This too was prohibited, as brown and darker peoples were told they were naturally impervious to culture or were thieves, rapists and sinners who had stolen language from others. The latter had more right to live. To Make X Great Again. When they died in the thousands during the initial skirmishes of the Second Civil War, the response was to retaliate in kind, killing infidels and sinners in the hundreds of thousands so that as to reassert their birth right to keep on living.

Soon, the ban on reading and storytelling was extended according to chance and convenience. Muslims were told to read their sacred book in the privacy of their homes and places of worship, for it was said that religion in the public realm was superstitious, the root of all evil, and should be confined to the domestic realm. Like women. The Churches themselves allowed for this separation, arguing that the private was, just as it was the case with the drives of the economy, a necessary pillar of the public.

This is the world as you found it. Ready-made. Discovered. Stitched up from one hundred million corpses. Unmade. Unmaking itself. Dismayed. Fanon lamented, "Yesterday, awakening to the world, I saw the sky turn upon itself utterly and wholly. I wanted to rise, but the disembowelled silence fell back upon me; its wings paralysed. Without responsibility, straddling Nothingness and Infinity, I began to weep."

39 In the Quarter of Savages

Some weeks ago, while contemplating the planets and the stars from the deck of the immerser sub-boat, you saw the sky turning upon itself utterly and wholly. You wanted to rise, but the disembowelled silence of the full moon fell back upon you as a giant white sea-monster.

You were paralysed.

Stuck between nothingness and infinity, you began to weep.

You did not move.

You could not move.

If you moved, time would move too.

Was it torture that stasis? On the contrary, you realized the stasis was life and the present between frames. You lingered there for what seems an eternity.

And quickly realised that on the far side of eternity is The Garden.

When you stopped crying, you were ready to face it. You went down and told your friends what had really happened. It's all a matter of geometry, you said to them. I merely escaped along the tangent. Knowing there is little room in this world for escapists and survivors, you and your friends realised the only way now was to become salvagers and savages.

The problem with survivors isn't that they survived the crumbling of the cities around them. Rather, in their survival they pose the challenge to others of surviving them. That is why survivors and salvagers are often the first to be branded savages, sacrificed and persecuted.

Oftentimes, such rituals of sacrifice are preceded by a ban and destruction of books and storytelling.

The immerser boat was full of them. Books. Some seven

thousand volumes in total. You hadn't seen this many after libraries were placed out of bounds to most people but those holding book-dealing licenses. Not since the Inquisition had been restored, and its policing branch, Autofaith, established.

Right then, you should have understood the significance of all those nights we spent together, reading stories before you went to sleep teaching you to read the pages down here as well as the stars above. Nobody else would do that for you.

For it was out of fashion, it was not legal.

But to me this was your initiation in magic. A dangerous kind of magic, I grant you that.

You should have realised it, but after I left you erased any memory of those days from your mind.

I should have told you this story back then, but I didn't. You can blame me for it. But now I'm telling you that it isn't too late to save your mirror-soul from the coming darkness.

Awakening to the world, you have now realised it is time you and your friends to go. Where? I don't know. To you it was a return. You could die here and now, and it would be all right. Time to find the place they call The Garden.

(Why? I don't want to die any more).

40   Damnation Abolition

The rules of commerce for the use of books were introduced early in the twenty-first century. Their principle was simple: if only a handful of people buy or rent a book, then it is appropriate to correct such commerce for efficiency reasons.

Two kinds of corrections were introduced.

They were known as damnation and abolition.

By damnation, a book could be rewritten in whole or part and an author or a book dealer would lose their license to trade or be declared infamous by order of the Council of World Faiths and the Ministry of Constancy.

By abolition, any trace of the author, her name and her work, could be erased from the records or withdrawn from the shelves of libraries, if any such books remained and their trade forbidden.

These measures were carried out by the civil servants of The Ministry, working together with the Council's censors. The latter became better known as Firemen or Inquisitors, and their enforcement arm as the Autofaith police. Initially, their task was to correct common errors detected in a published text, such as a perceived lack of coherence and constancy of belief in the main tenets of this or that faith whose Church collaborated with the Government in the provision of public services.

But when the Council became the main provider of education services in the country, a renewed effort to make reading lists and syllabuses constant and consistent with the pillars of morality gained ground.

Evolution was taught side by side with Intelligent Design, and the texts of Charles Darwin, Richard Dawkins and Hsia Qiwan were subtly sidelined in favour of more impartial accounts. From correcting partial errors in books,

Autofaith policemen moved onto withdrawing and actively pursuing certain titles and authors deemed infamous, or undeserving of attention and memory.

Successive conservative governments brought forward a number of Acts of Parliament that separated children's bookshops from adult bookshops, and created a licensing system for publishing houses, universities, newsprints, and Internet users and providers. Literature promoting atheism or agnosticism was discouraged, particularly if it was found to be associated with leftism or revolt.

The first public book burnings took place in England, the state of Arizona in the American south, and in Colombia and Chile more or less at the same time. It is not known whether they were ordered or spontaneous. Slowly but surely, under political pressure by the Council, the ritualistic burning of books caught on. Because of budgetary concerns, all public libraries disappeared. Only some private collections remained in Oxford and Cambridge subject to strict rules of licensing.

Reading became superfluous after the onset of smart implant technologies.

When we realised what had happened, it was too late. Most people adapted to this brave new world. Others left. Yet others were taken away because of their refusal to heed to the new modern order. In all cases we were left heartbroken, our hopes crushed after being separated from those we loved the most and which was closest to our hearts.

I do not seek your forgiveness or understanding. It is much too late for that, and it would be useless.

Rather, treat these words as a last will or a treasure map.

An invitation.

A gift, if you like.

To go downwards and venture into the realm of the

damned.

The journey will take a very long time. It may be eternal, but on the far side of eternity there is paradise. It is the place we set out to build, salvaging what we could from the ruins of the present.

Whatever we can salvage, half-destroyed manuscripts, books hidden for years in basements and cellars, hard disks and soft copies, we store in a fleet of submarines roaming the seas, making time until we can all reunite in the non-place that haunts every place, which they call The Garden.

It is my hope that if you read the signs, the books and the stars correctly, if you stop moving and contemplate the sun at eternal noon, you will find your way there.

I promise I will be there, waiting.

41 PA's Story

There must be some seven thousand volumes between hard copies and those stored in the memory banks of this sub, said PA. It is good business. Some people are ready to pay a hefty sum for a rare volume in the black market. Just as with drugs, cigarettes, unweapons and alcohol. It is a risk keeping them here, with Autofaith and eurosubs always on our asses. But if we manage to escape them the rewards can be handsome.

Don't get me wrong. We don't give a shit about the cultural suicide of western civilization or them stories about the emerald city they call The Garden. Those are children's tales. None of us know how to read. We have our implants for that. Your Colombian friend says he likes Conrad's *The Heart of Darkness* and Cervantes's *El Trato de Argel*. He got them, first editions, pristine condition, together with some old illuminated manuscript from someone in London who used to work as a librarian in St. Pancras. That's why we were there. That's what is supposed to be in the wooden crate, but we couldn't open it because they're vacuum sealed and protected against dampness and bugs.

They're expensive, but we already had a buyer in Spain. We got paid the first half in France and were supposed to deliver two nights ago in Barcelona. Freaking storm got in the way.

You see, I was going to retire with that money, said PA.

I don't mean getting myself into one of those Utopia vessels where the super-rich live, going from F1 in Dubai to the Cannes Festival in Paris and then to the fortress resorts in Asia and the Caribbean. I wouldn't make enough to do that. But your friend here says it would be just fine in Colombia, Argentina, or Brazil.

Now I'm thinking, what the hell, we can do with half the money. Like you, I want out of all this. The thing with the rich is they think money matters most, where it is a fact that in the end nothing does. Lo, you cannot take your riches into the next life.

It's like you say, we should move on.

I don't believe there's such a thing as The Garden, girl, but after all I've seen I'm ready for my little piece of paradise.

My story?

You really don't want to know my story of ashes and fire.

42   A Brief Story of Fire

Yesterday was for burning. I was there, not much older than a child with the Danish soldiers that were sent to fight the good fight for western civilization when the powder keg exploded in the south and the east.

Our commander was some English Lieutenant Colonel who took his orders from an American General. Ultimately, we were all in the service of some crazed demon.

Seven days after we entered the capital city, a crowd gathered in front of the national Library. At first, they were cautious, moved swiftly, but we were well aware of their presence, so they were fearful.

Their fear subsided when another group arrived in unmarked blue vehicles. First came the looters. They entered the Library knowing exactly where to look and what to look for. They grabbed the oldest manuscripts. Men, women, children, young and old, some were local while others had been brought there from without with the clear purpose of sowing chaos.

We were told we could not engage. Encouraged by our passivity, some among the looters began to place within the library the white phosphorous charges we ourselves had brought here. They knew what they were doing. Later on, it would be claimed that that charges had been stolen from us, but we just stood there and let it all happen. These men put the charges in the stacks and set them on fire, all the while chanting "Death to the dictator! Death to the apostate!" in English as well as Arabic. The journalists who were embedded with us captured the whole scene with their cameras, but I have never seen any of the images they got in our newstrips implants or uploaded on the web.

They made piles of books and burned them.

White phosphorous flames cannot be extinguished with water.

We have come a long way since Prometheus stole fire from Zeus's lightning bolt, concealed it in a hollow stalk of fennel, and gave it to us.

We have improved since the day the Water Spider brought a small coal of fire in the bowl that she spun from the thread coming out of her body.

But perhaps not much has changed.

Consider this. A long time ago the great Middle Kingdom Emperor Qin Shi Huangdi sent out orders for the immediate destruction of all books that defended a return to the traditional past. All books that did not deal with agriculture, medicine, or the art of astrological divination were thrown into the fire. He did so on the advice of his minister Li Si, who was one of the most prominent and well-read members of the legalist school of philosophy. Yet, this most advanced disciple of the legalist school had been everything but original in his zeal. Long before him, Lao Tzu had proposed in the Tao Te Ching to eliminate the wise and exile all geniuses, for that would be much more useful to the common sense of the people.

The lesson was learned by the Egyptians and their colonies in Greece. The ruler Akhenaten, who was also a poet, ordered all religious books that disagreed with his turn to monotheistic faith burned and replaced with tomes declaring the power of the Aten, the presence and horizon of the Sun. Athenian philosopher Plato, thinking insufficient the expulsion of all poets, dancers and musicians from his ideal city, sought also to burn the books in which his rival Democritus had laughed at the folly of human hubris and their belief that they could attain complete knowledge about the world of ideal forms that Plato had imagined.

In 331 BCE, Alexander the Great, a pupil of Aristotle

(who had in turn studied with Plato) marched against Babylon with an army of seven thousand men.

After crossing the Tigris and the Euphrates in the country we once knew as Iraq, Alexander, for that was his name, attacked the powerful and much more numerous armies of King Darius III. Alexander prevailed. An extremely beautiful courtesan named Thais asked Alexander to avenge the insults that the Persians had levied against the Greek for so long. Alexander ordered that the Palace of Persepolis should burn, together with the library that Darius had inherited from his ancestors Xerxes and Artaxerxes.

According to legend, Thais was in fact the human vessel and incarnation of the cursed demon Ahriman, and it was him who had inspired Alexander to burn all the books in Persepolis. He was trying to destroy one book in particular. Avesta, also known as the Truer Book of the Law.

The Avesta had been composed over the course of several thousand years, mostly out of oral stories, and was thought to contain the secrets of the unknown and the hidden creation. The story goes that whoever possesses the book can gain knowledge of the secret prayers and incantations, the passages and the ways that lead to the gates of the place where time exists on its own, unaccompanied by illusory motion. The ancient called that place and the conditions within it aša or existence, in which everything returns and yet nothing remains the same. In aša, the past, the present and the future bleed into one another and can be experienced as if they were one and the same. This is called the not-yet.

Others say it is not a place, a land, but the non-place that haunts every place. Like a river or a source, or the Path of the Anaconda for the Amerindians of Vaupes.

Like the fabled Source of Eternal Youth.

Eudemus of Rhodes thought of it as the coming of the new, a different beginning or second chance.

Chance determinant.

He said, "I shall converse with you staff in hand, and you will sit as you are sitting now, and so it will be in everything else." The place is mentioned in the stories about the return of the Messiah or the Buddha of the Mexican rainforest.

In the tales of King Arthur it is called Avalon.

And in the legend of Zarathustra, credited to have found it first and to have written about it in the Avesta.

Eloy Martinez found the entrance to it in a lounge bar of twentieth-century New Jersey.

This is the place they call The Garden.

The following lines are from the creature, as recorded by Laurie Sheck: "I am sitting on the bench with Eudemus. It's morning or afternoon or night. I watch his blue-veined hand curl around his staff. And I'm on the table where you made me. And in the forest alone, scavenging for food. I'm almost touching Claire's hand. I hear her slippery footsteps on the stairs. Her face is young then older then young again. Over and over Socrates is born, lives, dies. Zhuangzi dreams himself a butterfly. Or a butterfly dreams himself Zhuangzi." [4]

Borges wrote, "it is the tiger which destroys me but I am the tiger."

And the creature, "all this ice I feel inside me, and the night ... as if such things could be measured, as if there weren't this fire in the skull, and in that fire a hand."

And in that fire, which you know so well, dear you, a woman now no longer a little girl, the voice says: "fire is in hair, and this way come in of I's head, and of I's belly, that a gleaning is come in of I with fire. It is not glean of I, but glean of fire." [5]

Then, you opened your mouth to say a word and it

---

[4] Credit to L Sheck, *A Monster's Notes* (A. Knopf, 2012) 14-5.
[5] Credit to A Moore, *The Voice of the Fire* (Top Shelf, 2003) 60.

hurt you, for it was fire that came through your mouth. It rose and rose. Like a column of air in the desert. With grits of bright, lighting up the old black sky.

Was this Moore the author or Ahriman the Demon?

Ahriman the demon talked through Thais who talked to Alexander who burned Persepolis and the holy book with it. But there are those who say he took it with him back to Greece with the treasure carried by 20,000 mules and 5,000 camels. Others say it was reconstructed by memory under orders of the Sassanid prince Ardasir and deposited in the library at Alexandria by Demetrius before he was killed by an asp the same as all the other librarians who died cruel deaths. Including Theon, whose daughter Hypatia wrote about the book in the Almagest. Also destroyed. Violated and lost, like her.

It is said that Cyril, a nephew of the Patriarch Archbishop of Alexandria, and the man who would bring about the destruction of the library, could not tolerate that a woman's wisdom would cast doubt upon the doctrines of the Christ. He was eaten up by jealousy. In 415 AD he plotted the murder of Hypatia. Under his orders, a certain Peter led a mob that seized Hypatia while she was delivering a lecture and accused her of being a witch, as befits such occasions.

No one helped her. Not even the one among her students who had proclaimed to love her more than life itself. The Christians led by Peter dragged Hypatia from her hair to the Cesarion church, where they ripped her clothes apart and raped her one after the other. Hypatia had remained celibate until then. The people of Alexandria watched on while the mob brutally beat Hypatia with roof tiles. Death by stoning, and not a Jesus in sight to stop it. No demon slayer.

She died, it is said, reciting an equation from Diophantus's Arithmetica. Others insist she passed on while whispering a Zoroastrian incantation from the Avesta in the name of Ahriman. Frightened that Hypatia could rescue herself from the clutches of death, the monks carried her body to a place known as Cinarus and tore it apart.

They disembowelled Hypatia's corpse with knives prepared specially for the ritual by the archbishop Theophilus. A rival demon called Nebiros had instructed archbishop Theophilus on the manner of the ritual that had to be performed in order to stop Hypatia coming back from the dead. Her internal organs and bones were removed and thrown into a pile of fire.

Yet, such horrors were insufficient to conjure away the shadow of the holy book from the mind of Archbishop Teophilus of Alexandria and his nephew.

Nebiros had not had enough.

Later on, the monks at the service of Cyrilus and the archbishop incited the mob to loot and burn the library. It was the year 391 AD. Theophilus, once a fanatical reader of Origen of Alexandria in whose writings he learned first about the existence of the book Avesta that describes the path towards the garden of immortality, later turned into the most vicious enemy of everything he thought derived from the mind of his former favourite mentor and author.

In particular, his teachings on the pre-existence of time, space and souls independently of the movement that incarnates them in human bodies. This notion, and the doctrine that in the end even the devil would be reconciled with God, proved to Theophilus that his former master had been seduced and corrupted by the secrets of the Avesta, hidden somewhere in the Library of Alexandria.

It had to be destroyed.

Of course, the story does not end there. During the caliphate in Spain, Hakam II instructed his advisors to seek copies of all the best books in the world. Four hundred thousand volumes dealing with all aspects of the human, the unhuman and the non-human were deposited in the library he founded in Córdoba.

Reputedly, Hakam read them all. But he was most interested in a tract that was mentioned in a now lost page of the letter that general Amr Ibn sent to Mohammed's successor, Omar, once the conquest of Egypt was completed.

The letter was an inventory of the buildings and objects of value found in Alexandria. It is said it contains a detailed account of an inner vault encountered intact under the ruins of the temple of Serapis. According to the general, within it there was only one book. The ancient roll known as Avesta.

General Amr asked the monarch what should be done with the scroll. King Omar responded in a letter that Amr read to the respected commentator of Aristotle, John Philoponus, the following: "With regard to the book you mention, here is my answer. If it contains the same doctrine as the Qur'an, it is useless for it merely repeats; if it is not in agreement with the doctrine of the Qur'an, there is no reason to save it."

They both received such news with much sadness. Wishing not to disobey a direct order of the successor of the Prophet, they settled upon interpreting such commands in accordance to the letter. John Philoponus was given the task of studying the book in order to pass judgment on its usefulness and consistency with the teachings of the Qur'an. To do so, John had to produce a perfect copy of the holy book of the Zoroastrians, a task in which he achieved such degree of excellence and perfection that it would have been completely impossible for anyone to distinguish the copy from the original.

Amr carried out the orders of his King. Whatever remained of the Library of Alexandria was put to the fire and completely destroyed. The general's conscience was calm, for he thought he had been obedient in burning the actual book while secretly preserving a copy. Some historians believe that the copy was burned in the pyre while the original found its way to Hakam's fabled library.

Upon his death, Almanzor took control of the al-Andalús. A frustrated writer, Almanzor allowed zealous advisers to burn all the books not held to be sacred by Muslims. They were piled up and the pyre burned for almost an entire year. It is said that none of the books once contained in Hakam's library survived until the present.

This is not true. There is proof that the teachings contained in the Zoroastrian Book of the Law Avesta survived in the work of the mysterious Johannes Scotus Erigena, also known as John the Scott. Like John Philoponus, he too was considered a rebellious heretic. In De Predestinatione, John the Scott argued that no one, not even the devil, is condemned to hell forever because God is omnipotent and in the end all those who came from him would return to him, again and again. His controversial De Divisione Natura was burned in a public bonfire, but that did not stop the likes of Giordano Bruno, Artemisia Gentileschi, Pico della Mirandola or Baruch Spinoza, and thereafter Juana Ines de la Cruz, from defending John Scott's thesis that there are worlds within worlds which it is possible to cross and enter for anyone in possession of the right key. The gate which such key belongs to is known as the Garden's Gate.

Such ideas were taken by John the Scott and his successors in Christian Europe from the writings of Dyonisus the Areopagite, and from Arabic and Jewish sources, including the Ziyyuni, attributed to the Kabbalist Menahem Zioni, and the so-called Testament of Solomon also known as The Lost Key. Such tracts and the wisdom within them made it via Córdoba in Spain into Italy and the Americas. In the latter, they merged with the teachings of the tlamantineme and later on with the images produced by a band of brothers and sisters known as Gesta Barbara in Bolivia. Copies of the Ziyyuni were burned in Italy in 1559, together with the Talmud, the works of Moises ben Maimon, and the Toledot Yeshu in which the figure of Jesus is said to be denigrated by being modelled upon that of Zarathustra.

Surely, few of the book burners of the 1500s compare to the zeal and commitment shown by the Franciscan monk Francisco Jimenez de Cisneros, named Archbishop of Toledo by her Catholic Majesty Isabella of Spain. His aim was to strike fear into the hearts of all Muslims, Jews, Tupies and others branded infidels, whether they lived in newly conquered Granada, in North Africa, or in the New World stolen from the American Indians.

He imposed clerical celibacy, advised King Ferdinand and Queen Isabella of Spain to expel the Jews and tortured thousands in order to persuade them to abandon their faith and convert to the doctrine of the Christ. In the process, the Crown could take over their riches, which is the true cause of the wealth of nations. He also shared with fellow Franciscans Juan de Zumarraga and Diego de Landa a vicious form of self-righteousness and conviction that led them to bring about the integration of a new culture by destroying and subordinating those that existed in the Americas.

The three of them embarked on a crusade to erase any trace of the Truer Law, whether it was the creolised version or the one originated in the writings of the Avesta.

In 1530, Zumarraga brought about the end of days for the people of Texcoco in Mexico. Gathering all the writings and the speaking pictures of the Mexica and the Maya, he made a bonfire. Those who witnessed understood well that his intention was to obliterate the past once and for all in order to give way to a brave new age.

It was a similar gesture that I witnessed as I stood

passively, just another member of the Danish Army sent to fight for freedom in the Middle East. When the National Library was looted and burned to the ground.

Our lonely impunity is rank. It smells to the heavens. We did as de Alba and Zumarraga did. They who fathered Goebbels on 10 May 1933 in the Orpenplatz of Berlin, who, in turn, gave way to the OAS on 6 June 1962 after the referendum on Algerian independence, and to bishop Nikon Mironov of Ekaterinburg who ordered the burning of all treatises urging the Russian Orthodox Church dialogue with other creeds.

We mirrored Ramon Serrano Suñer, who admired Goebbels and masterminded censorship and destruction in the Spain of Generalísimo Francisco Franco, Caudillo of Spain by the Grace of God, who fathered Augusto Jose Ramon Pinochet Ugarte of Chile. In September 1973, the latter ordered an attack on Quimantó and commanded that all the books produced there and destined to the socialist island of Cuba should be torn apart and cut to pieces.

Perhaps he had in mind the monks of Cyril of Alexandria.

If our impunity is allowed to persist, and our deed forgotten, then we shall shamefully vindicate the ancient words of the Truer Book of the Law, the Avesta, according to which the justice of this world is like cobwebs, strong enough only to contain the weak.

We did the deed of an old crazed devil and remain indebted to him.

One day he shall come to collect my soul.

So says the voice of the fire, the voice burning in my head, loud and clear like the unceasing beating of drums or the roar of the thunder.

I have witnessed the end of days and will do so again.

43 Nebiros

Now you know, Clara said.

Our PA is a drummer, continuously listening to the beat in his head. He says it is the voice of the fire.

He says he tried to reclaim an old-looking tract from one of the looters, a boy, no older than ten, who cursed him.

He believes he's cursed. He says one day that devil will return to reclaim payment of his debt.

44   Palabrero

The tale is told of the Maya and Carib men and women of the word, known merely as palabreros.

They memorized the verses of the Book of the People to save its contents from the fire lighted by de Landa and Cisneros and passed its verses and speaking pictures onto their children so that they will pass them onto their children, and so on and so forth with no end.

Enquiring about this manifestation of the infinite, chronicler Diego Duran speculated that the Book of the People resembled other books of Arabic and Persian origin, perhaps even some older tracts, which refer to a key that opens the gates to a garden where all of time exists at once.

In the Book of the People, the world in which we live was created by the twins Hun Ahpú and Hun Camé. The twins were destined to be rivals for all time, like Ahriman and Nebiros-Ormudz in the story told in the Avesta. Like them, Hun Ahpú and Hun Camé were the twin siblings of a supreme and abstract principle, a god if you will, the deity that represents time without condition or movement, the one that always divides into two.

To settle their quarrel and give way to the world in which you and your friends exist, Hun Ahpú had to descend into the realm of the damned. There, she had to find and wage war against Hun Camé so that the sun, imprisoned in the bowels of the earth, could once more shine eternal at noon and allow everything above to live again. In the tale of the Maya, the twins fight together and fight one another, for they are opposites, the result of one divided into two.

Hun Ahpú was afraid when she began her journey through the oceans and the forest of language.

Like you are now.

She asked her friend Ixbalanqué to accompany her. Ixbalanqué loved her very dearly.

He said yes.

He chose two of his best warriors among the first people, a boy and a girl, to join their quest.

Together, the four of them travelled the blackened water that separated the city surface from the cavernous kingdom of death down below. The sea was dangerous, full of creatures that may appear friendly at first but will try to kill you while you sleep.

Hun Ahpú was afraid, because at sea and in language nothing is what it appears to be. The dark seas, the forest of language, and the kingdom of death were no simple space but also a state of the soul, or all of these things at once. As you now know, in the dark real things do not seem more real than in dreams. But on the other side of the sea there is a place, a non-place that haunts every place.

A forest.

A garden made out of words.

In the first and most exterior part of the garden words are read the same forward and downward. In there, you and your friends should be careful, you must remain watchful because it is all too easy to get lost in the maze of acrostic words.

The entrance to the garden is guarded by seven spirits whose names you must learn to pronounce beforehand if you want to control them. This is crucial, since they will try to control you and drive you to madness. If you and your friends succeed, then you will arrive at the second level of the garden in which words read differently forward and downward. If it is easy to get lost in the labyrinth of acrostic words, things are a lot worse in the second level, for it is a Moebius band-like series of tunnels and corridors extending throughout the garden. Here you will need all the help you can get from your friends. For here seven superior beings, seven demons roam these corridors and tunnels hiding between the lines and in the empty spaces that separate one letter from the next.

Nebiros is one of them.

I cannot tell you about the third and innermost part of The Garden, which is also the most dangerous. No one has made it there yet. No one who has survived to tell the tale. All we know is this: in the third square garden words read the same forward, backward, downward, and upward. Here the principal spirits live. We do not know their number.

But we know Ahriman is one of them.

At the centre of The Garden there is a gate.

The gate guards the entrance to a staircase which seems infinite and descends into the realm of the dead. This world down below is called Xibal. It is the exact counterpoint to the surface of the earth. It will present you always with the inverted face of the people and the things which are most familiar to you, and you will not be able to distinguish between them.

You and your friends must travel there, and conquer Hun Camé, which is Death, so that the sun will rise again and be eternal.

This is the same as what the mosquito bird told Hun Ahpú.

And then, she was even more scared.

Oh, and beware, said the mosquito bird.

For in the labyrinths, the corridors, and the tunnels of the garden there is no time. Down here time is being abolished. This is the place where time no longer destroys, and it is called Oxkintok.

This is what Raven, the mosquito bird said.

This is what the Book of the People says.

45   Carry Your Demons with You

You saw her coming in the night. You were on deck. Like every other night, trying to read the planets and the stars to find safe passage for you and your friends. You had been given a quest: find The Garden, name the demons, gain them. Carry your demons with you. To the gate. Let them guide you down below. Defeat Death. Let the sun rise again. Isn't this what all tales tell? Meanwhile, you thought, it would be safe here in the boat with your friends. Here in the immerser, you thought, I am inside a womb whose walls are shelves filled with books. Some seven thousand volumes to search for signs, clues, maps, spells, names. The others didn't need to know you could read those pages. Boys don't like girls who read.

(And you wanted PA to like you. He told you to call him Pierre).

You spent a lot of free time together. You would tell each other stories about the place they call The Garden, where it would be possible to restore all the lost books. You told him he and the others would have to help you going through the three levels of the forest of words to get to the gate at the centre of The Garden. You told him: if one has the key to that door, and possesses the names of the spirits who guard it, then it would be easy to find the staircase into the world down below. And in that world all the books that have been lost persist in quiet sleep, waiting to be brought back to the light since in the darkness no one reads them any more. It would be like vanquishing Death itself. Then, all the books would fill once more the shelves of the Library of Alexandria and be read again. You told Pierre: as you can see this is not always a rational matter. It's merely geometry. Pierre loved you telling that story. As days passed, he came to think that in this god-forsaken world it would mean something to rebuild the Library at Alexandria. He sent messages to all the other subs out there, telling them it was time to stop running, hiding from the inquisitors and the Council. Time to start reclaiming some space, a no-place. To take it and occupy it. To salvage what you could from each other. To raise and set alight a beacon in Faro island. It would be a house light, standing tall and erect so that all could see it from afar and allow some hope in their hearts. That even if the world had ended there was now a place to gather and be. A hall, a temple for the rising sun, an academy and a library. He told them this would be their purpose from now on. To rebuild the library and museum of Alexandria. It was simple, it was practical. Make all the boats go to their places of delivery and salvage as many books as they could. Copy all the files from the servers, reclaim all the precious manuscripts kept in cellars, backrooms, and basements. Board all Utopia ships and take over the invaluable rolls they paid so much to possess. After all, it isn't stealing if you take what has been stolen already. Then take it all to Alexandria. Isn't there a free port already in the hands of rebellious Greek and Egyptians? It should be possible to defend it from the Europeans and the Council. No Autofaith, no inquisition, no Zumarraga and no Theophilus. No implant tech and no religion there. We will have to learn to read again, said Pierre. You figured they had listened and sent one to talk to Pierre directly. A woman. You saw her first from your post on top of the deck. She was wearing a long black dress covering her body from the neck all the way down to her toes. It was tight at the torso and the waist. With the help of a long-eye it was easy to spot the stranger was a tall woman. She was also wearing a tall black hat with a wide brim, and on top of it a veil made out of black lace covering her pale face and black hair. You thought she looked beautiful. She seemed to be travelling alone, in a vessel that from the distance seemed less like a boat and much more like a black vintage car. Jackie O arriving on the back of her black Lincoln Continental, you joked in the intercom. The reference was lost on Clara and your Colombian friend. Not on Pierre. Your Colombian friend had spotted her already in the negsonar he had built with the pieces of implant tech he had collected from each another. His pet project during these months in the high seas. Looks like a small sub, just enough for one person. Impossible to detect it by anyone other than me, he said. Clara was already charging the unweapon. The vessel's approach was slow. The mist, her attire, the sudden calm of the seas, the absence of noise, everything gave you the impression of a funeral motorcade. As her small boat came about, the woman moved behind the steering wheel of the black vintage car. A couple of drones that looked more like plastic mannequins sat in the rear of the car. It changed course and stopped right beside your immerser. You extended your hand to help her come aboard. As soon as she touched you, everything went blank. By the time your senses came back, the woman in black had gone inside, Clara was lying unconscious beside you and the corridors of the boat were immersed in darkness. The walls were covered with letters written in blood, in a language you couldn't understand. Water was quickly filling up the engine room and the bridge. In the bridge you found the body of your Colombian friend floating among the debris. Through the porthole you saw the blackened skies, and a tempest moving swiftly towards the boat. You panicked at the sight of what looked like a whirlwind of insane flying machines filling the sky. As it came closer, the cloud revealed itself as a swarm of the dead of the Popham massacre. You ran to your quarters, looking for the mirror you kept under the pillow. As you ran back to the cargo bay, mirror in hand, time seemed to slow down. In the corner of your eye you caught a glimpse of the swarm of the dead traversing the vessel, breaching the haul before returning to the sky where it remained in stasis like a cloud of vaporising angels of death. Then, you saw the woman in the black dress walking among the fractured profiles of the dead. A series of landscapes appeared before you. A regatta of corpses sailing pass the remains of the city of London; the gigantic statues of Ramses and his wife in Luxor, destroyed by eurodrones; a young woman being torn apart in the Cesarion; your mother suspended in mid-air, swallowed by a sea of flames; straight ahead, on the other side of the door separating the cargo bay, Pierre's body in a pool of what seemed like dark blood. You stopped at the entrance, holding up the mirror in front of the woman in the black dress. She was kneeling down beside Pierre, drawing a diagram of bones on his chest using her long fingernails. You shouted at her. You will not go until I set you up a mirror glass, where you may see the inmost part of you! I will put you to death so that you may free him, my Pierre, if he is now your slave! The woman stood up and turned towards you. Every child, as they grow up, she said, keeps a mirror underneath their pillow. Look in it and you will see what you will become, a creature fallen from grace. This fate you must confront as a condition of his salvation. Do you want him? I will give you his mirror-soul, but know this, that you will be the cause of his fall or his redemption. You not I. For at the moment he looks into his mirror he will fall into mortal danger, tempted into a despair that will make his emptiness irrevocable. He will be soulless and will feel exactly as you feel right now: that it is impossible to face such solitude and live. I shall give you his mirror, which I possess, so that he sees in it an illusory companion. But only in exchange for the one you now hold against me. So that you go without a soul, not him. His, in exchange for yours.   The lights went out once more. When you woke up, Pierre was holding your head urging you to drink some water. Clara was also there, shaken. The body of your Colombian friend lied beside you on the floor. His face was shredded, and there were multiple cuts in his arms and torso. He won't make it, Clara said. She fooled us all, Pierre said. She introduced herself as a member of our pack. She used our codes and our signals. How could I've known she was in fact an inquisitor? No wonder she took me straight to the cargo bay. She was after the contents of the wooden crate. She made me open it. Almost killed me in the process. You scared her. I don't know how. I've never seen anyone survive an encounter with an inquisitor. You saved me. How? I made a pact, you said. I gave her my mirror.

46   Notes on the Making of Pacts with Demons

It is said in this tale that there're two sorts of people. The self-appointed builders of the future, on the one side. On the other, the untimely. Branded savages by anathema, these were expelled to the fringes of the world. Marked as dwellers of the past, they were condemned by the builders to roam the deserts of the gap.

Builders live in constant fear of their return, and wage war to defer the day when the damned may come back from exile in the desert to reclaim their lands. Builders have scorched the skies and closed all the gates to stop them. They've hidden all the keys inside seven rings hidden inside seven obsidian mirrors. In such mirrors, builders do not see you and me and the others they wish to lock in the out; they only see themselves.

The gap is the source of our power. The desert is the source of power. There we cannot be seen; there we can move between frames. To any place and time. We aren't eternal, but timeless. They call us savages, the resistant dead, for we keep returning from the brink of extinction.

Coming back from the mass graves and the pyramids of coffins with no bodies in them.

You, and me and all the others whom they accuse of crimes against the property and propriety of this reality.

We, the disappeared.

Fear them not, for we have turned their accusation back against them.

We call them devourers of time, unmakers of history.

Let us call ourselves something else, a name they will fear.

This is the name you must use in the making of a pact. The name is Legion.

An infernal storm, a tempest repeating itself day and night broke up when the inquisitor boarded our boat. We were attacked. Our cargo raided. Pretending to be one of us, the inquisitor tricked us. We were left at the mercy of a black army of insane machines.

Our vessel was nearly destroyed. Our mechanic now lies in sickbay somewhere between life and death.

After the attack, the inquisitor took with her the contents of a wooden crate entrusted to us under seal, a leather-bound copy of the Twenty Second Epistle of the Brethren of Purity. And the girl's mirrorsoul.

The girl saved our lives.

We shall follow the inquisitor and recover the mirror. But unforgiving conditions conspire against our salvage effort. Every time we come close enough to use the unweapon and disarm her vessel, the wind grows more furious and violent undersea currents threaten to crush us. The girl without name, given though she is to fantastic stories and inventions has assured to us with all seriousness that the ship of the inquisitor has turned into a Haploteuthis Ferox; a predatory cephalopod often seen in the seas and the desert, rising like an unforgiving god to feed on the lost.

The girl says she can break us free from its tentacles.

Some of the things she says make little sense to me. She speaks of a swarm of dead souls, her mother among them, wrapped around the boat like a vampire squid sucking the life out of our mirror-souls.

Superstition aside, this storm does behave as if it were the pet god of some wicked sorceress.

48 Mirrorsoul (Sampled Dub)

If a mirror can hold
  a soul,
  and an algorithm
      may reduce to numbers
        the essence of a person,
    then perhaps a word   or a likely likeness
        might be able to let inside
    the outside fury of the wind
    the violence of the sea currents.
                    Let the outside
      in,
          to rise up instead
                  a Universal Army,
        or the hope of communion.
          For something unspeakable
              has happened in this world.
  It does mean something
      something unspeakable
        to have been born
          the way you were born.
  In a white world,
      an anti-sexual world
      an anti-human world
  A world of volatile appearances,
  an algorithm may reduce to numbers
      the essence of a person
  and made it easy to separate
      the apparent from the existent.
  This is precisely what the present order's mythology
continues to exploit.
      It turns appearances

into refractions,
     like mirages.
Refractions of desire.
     In fact,
        a single desire.
The desire for more.
    To keep all of the more and more.
     To keep everything for you,
        and keep to oneself.
The result is unsettling:
    there is more solitude
          in
          side
inner
most
       isolation
   more
   pain,
more
dereliction.
And yet, nothing is private.
Not even pain and dereliction
Not even the physical aspects of desire, the existent.
The body
   Disappears.
We live within spectacle.
     It would take a mirror,
       and the rays of the sun
         to straighten that bend.
It does mean something
     something unspeakable
      to have been born
        the way you were born.
Black in a white world.

You very soon,
            abandon all hope
                        to rise up instead
                        a Universal Army,
            or the hope of communion.
Thus,
            we have become like those immobilised characters
of theatre.
            Not scrunched into trash cans, as in Endgame.
            But confined all the same to a narrow loop.
            Marked people look up
                        or look down
                                    (mostly)
            But do not look at each other,
                        not at you,
                                    and people with unworn white masks,
                        mainly,
                                    look away.
            We live within spectacle.
            It would take a mirror,
                        and the rays of the sun
                                    to straighten
                                    that
                                    b
                                                end.
And the universe?
            "The universe is simply a sounding drum."
Says the blues line
            of brother Fire Next Time.
                                    Fail.
                                    Fail again.
Says the blues line of brother Waiting in Line.
            Waiting for a god who will never come.
                        We live within spectacle.

It would take a mirror,
                    and the rays of the sun
                              to straighten that b   end.
The Winter Palace has been taken,
not by blacks or reds   by refractions
of a single desire.
          Persons who want to disavow
                    any difference or distinction between a life
          in pleasure and desire
and another life
          in automated destruction
                              a world of happy suicides,
who would like to have it all,
          all of the more and more
to keep everything for themselves
          and keep to themselves
To reach the highest peaks of experience
And Ornament before in their wake,
          the storm takes it all away.
We live in the storm called spectacle.
It would take a mirror,
          and the rays of the sun
          to straighten that.

How then to remind the giant, whose foot-tentacle is
crushing your neck,
          the universe is not merely the stars and the moon and
the planets,
          flowers, grass and trees, but other people just as well? [6]

---

[6] These lines are not mine but mere samples, borrowings and theft. I have looted from
Claude the anthropologist, Peter the German, James the Fire Next Time and Samuel
Waiting in Line. But I'm not the only thief, not even a thief. I learned from the best. I
learned from them.

49 Not-Yet (Re-Sampled Dub)

How then to remind the giant,
whose foot is crushing our neck
that the universe has evolved no terms for your existence,
Not-yet.
Not-yet.
And if you despair
At the lack of human love,
God's love alone is left.
But God,
as brother Fire says,
is white,
and he has left.
What then?
Fail.
Fail again.
As brother Waiting says.

50 Pulse Dub

It would take a mirror,
     and the rays of the sun
          to straighten that b   end.
Hold up that mirror
        to the beast's face,
            its controller
         remind the beast,
and her,
     they're trapped
        not inside a bottle or a lamp
           in a fantasy of their own making.
It is an old dream
in which the joys eternally denied to W/Man,
are removed to an equally unattainable
                 Future or Past.
The former placing the end of innocent lies
at a time when the confusion of words and unlikely lies
made languages
     into refractions of a single desire,
     the latter describing
     the bliss of the hereafter
as a heaven where W/Man can keep for h/self
all of the more and more
all the women
all the girls.
     The Future or Past
        of a world in which one might keep to oneself.
It would take a mirror,
    and the rays of the sun
        to straighten that b   (end).

51 F.T.A

In all the old stories,
>> the stories I told you when you were still a little girl,
>>> such a thing was possible.
Hold up a mirror
> to show the beast the true
>> likely image.
Of its master puppeteer.
Invite the storm
> to join you in the uprising.
>> Why not now?
It would only take the right words and some images.
Likely images.
> Battle of Algiers.
>> Born in Flames.
>> Punishment Park, or
>>> Land and Freedom.
Guns & Poetry
>> (An Organisation of Dreams)
>> A Place of Rage, or
>> Hour of the Furnaces.
>>> you
>>> Salt of the Earth.
>>> you
>>> When I Saw You
>>> and your friends
Chocolate Babies
>> You
Warrior Women
>> Sorry to Bother You
but you have
>> Finally Got the News

that the time has come for you to become
The Spook Who Sat by the Door
An Anarchist from the Colony
The Body (that) Remembers When the World Broke
Open
and go
Palante, Siempre Palante
and say
Soy Cuba
I am Not Your Negro
but a
Zapantera Negra
and
Strike
Now!
(against the background sound of a)
Black Power Mixtape. F. T. A.

52 | I'm Drum

If the inquisitor sorceress controls water and air through the one she has turned into a slave it may be worth showing to the giant in chains a likely image. It may be worth showing the giant storm that exists between you water and air how to change course how to lower speed and turn against its master. As in La Nouvelle Colonie ou la Ligue des femmes. As in L'Ile des esclaves. Or in Caliban it would be possible to hold up a mirror to its face until it can contemplate its true and likely image. Right now, the storm does resemble a giant darkening the sky before rolling down to the surface of the sea and gathering itself into a great rumble. It appears like a blue giant, his head as high as a dome touching the clouds while his feet rest on the ground somewhere in the bottom of the ocean. It wouldn't be too far-fetched to imagine the hands of this giant storm as gigantic pitchforks holding & rocking your boat or the tentacles of a titan crushing your vessel, and its boot on your neck doing the bidding of its master, asphyxiating you. Picture, then, this giant with legs as tall as the mast of an old ship his ears as shields with pendants made out of the dust of stars and the luminescence of the creatures of the abyss. One says murder. The other says kill. The giant is terrifying. It seems he aims to end you. But in fact he's only doing the bidding of his master. It is not impossible, therefore, to think that all this howling comes from an open mouth as big as a cavern, or an underwater volcano, its boots as rocks being expelled by an eruption deep underneath the surface of the sea, or the hour of our furnaces. Picture his nostrils as trumpets announcing the end of days and his one eye like a cinema projector. A single light beam. If all this is real and possible, then it might be possible too to picture the howling is in fact a language, to believe that the tempest speaks

and talk back
and shout at him
and reproach him.
Has he forgotten who he was?
Has he forgotten what he did?
Has he forgotten that in anger and fury the giant cursed
both God and King Solomon?
For having imprisoned him all these years
In shackles.
And in other's shackles.

Now by the evil ways of a sorceress, the blue giant obeys their will. The will of sorceress Prosper and her King. Do remind the giant Jinn that the sorceress and the King, the King and his citizens, the city as a whole, and each individual in it have their own fantasy of the workings of demons and the gods. Shout back at him and denounce it as false; the relationship between demons and gods (the blue giant, the storm) and their worshippers; for it is a contract. Not a gift, but a contract. Sealed with the help of the clergy & the sorceress. For sure, these men and women perceive demons and deities only through a glass darkly; and have a less clear perception of their nature than they have of the deities' labours on their behalf. And they seek to repay them by efforts of their own. For sure. This is how the seed of a bad idea grew in them that God and men have mutual claims on each other. That service, incantation and worship is rendered in the expectation of some other service in return. This is a bad idea and it carries within two dangers. One is spectacle. Hubris is the other. One is the husk of the outer appearance. The shimmering. The sorceress magic carries within it that danger of illumination reduced to the outer side of ritual. Therein lies her strength, also her weakness. By hubris, the sorceress and her King turn the tables on God whom they threaten by denying him performance of the cult. This is how the gods, facticius, God and the Jinn came to be shackled by men. This is how the world of fables and myths died. When Aurelius Augustinus, first of the inquisitors, condemned the fabulous theology of the ancients offering in its stead the natural logos & word of the City of God, as the only true logos & word and the Emperor King as the only true representative of logos & the word. That offer was accepted but it was from the outset a poor replacement leaving in its wake only the husk of the outer appearance.

The shimmering.

The false.

Our aim is the opposite of Aurelius Augustine's.
To recover the myths & fables of the poets and their theatrical theology which took place on the stage and circuses of Rome, which took place on the stage of the Mexica juego de pelota.

Our magic is not same.

Our magic is different.
It takes the shape of saturnales galantes and ludi scenicae. On our stage the sacred gods are made to appear and celebrated with music, orgies and games in their most immoral in their own shame. Anubis the Adulterer. The Moon Man. The Flagellation of Diana. The Starving Hercules. The Exiled Serpent. The Shackled Jinn. The Fallen King. And if the purpose of the King's cult and the magic of the sorceress is to bind gods and demons to their service, as a prelude to the enslavement of women and men, ours is different, ours is negligence. Of both God and the cult. We do not aim to free kings and men from their veneration of money, but to liberate the Money God and all others from their veneration. We aim to forget them. We aim to let go of demons and gods. For only then women and men can also let go of their voluntary slavery.

53 Workplay

And   work

        And   play.

And   work.

        And   play.

54 Drum Running Down

This is what Smenkhare taught us.
  She who became him who became her.
  She was the first of our kind.
The first black woman warrior.
  Not the wife of the king
  ta hemet nesu
  but Dahamunzu
the first woman to become man to become woman
  determined to forge alliances
  with former enemies
  to eat flowers with them.
For this she was branded a traitor
  Silenced
  Erased from the records
  Marked as a witch,
  Judged as one by the inquisitors
  Who wished to burn her at the stake
  To tame her body
  To rape her
  & then to stone her
  quarter her,
  to exorcise every memory of her,
  after the Restoration.

55 Hoodoo

Her spirit lives on
    brave and rebellious,
    she lives on
    in you.
Her teachings
    in you
    in artwork and simulacra
    and in the collaboration of former enemies and demons
    in artwork and simulacra.
When artists create a work,
    the way you create your drawings, images and mirrors
    uploading them in the stream
    this is the burning of the husk of the outer appearance.
    The key / riddle / secret
    as the question you have been asking all your life
    enters into the realm of ideas.
This is how we pass from outer substance to inner idea,
    and from the shimmering to the secret sun within
    without ever abandoning the surface
    in order to come back to the surface
    to the common here & now
    and bring with us the rays of the sun
    to illuminate the cavern of our slavery.
    And lift the veil.

A destruction of the work
how the external form achieves
its bright
est degree of illumination.
We go in to let the outside in.
We let go of the phantasm,
as you have let go of your mirror-soul
so as to place it in simulacra
a drawing
an image
a photograph
a poem
a mirror
uploading them in the stream.
What accounts for the power of a work is the movement
of a demonic presence. Coming-and-going-coming-and-
becoming between you the artist and the artwork, your fetish
& the simulacrum, and between the fetish & its viewers. This
constant changing and morphing intensifies the view of the
contemplator & the feelings the contemplator has attached to
the events of the past latent but never finished. Therefore, also
the whole of history she's pregnant with possibilities latent
but never finished. This constant changing and morphing is
the same as the nature of the Jinn.

Demons are never identical to themselves.
What returns acts differently in the artist & the simulacrum
& its audience.
Producing them & the future.
Both difference and orientation.
A gift.
This
is what we call love.

57 Shine

Such is the meaning & sense of the demon before you.
        He doesn't mean to attack you,
        but was ordered to do so
        for he had promised never to disobey his master
        under threat of being chained
        & shackled.
But if all this is true, then it must also be true
        what the old tales tell.
        That the warrior girl reproached the giant with fire
this time.
        That the warrior girl reproached the giant with just
revelation this time.
        That the warrior girl created a work of art
        which imitated the phantasm
        & projected its exorcised spirit
        from the girl's soul
        into simulacra.
        A sculpture, a fetish, a mirror-image, a photograph.
        You made.
        And in it
        the mirror-image shows Kings Akhenaten, Solomon &
Shango.
All the patriarchs
        Dead for thousands of years.
        The image reveals the answer
        to the question you have been asking all these years
        that we live at the other end of time
        and that another end of the world is possible.
        This is what you, warrior girl,
        have made present to the
        Jinn of the giant storm

And to all of us by means of art.
A just revelation. A revolution.
From here onwards is up to us
to decide
fall or fly?

58 Arrival

As the Jinn prepared to unleash a most violent gust upon your boat you told him to consider the following riddle.

That the Jinn had been right all along.

That there is no God.

And if there is no God, you need not obey the commands of kings and their inquisitors.

You and I are one in this refusal.

You said

In it I can become you and you become me.

And in it, here and now, you and I can be free.

We have arrived.

Here.

I'm here.

59   Nohor

On 23 November, 1492, Columbus wrote: "They speak of an island, which they say was very large and that on it lived people who had only one eye and others called cannibals, of whom they seem to be very afraid." On 11 December, 1492, he observed: "Caniba refers in fact to the people of El Gran Can." The Caniba, were also known as the Cariba, Calib or Caribes. In the letter of 15 February, 1493 in which Columbus announces his discoveries to the world, he wrote: "I have found, then, neither monsters nor news of any save for an island called Quarives, the second upon entering the Indies, which is populated with people held by everyone on the islands to be very ferocious, and who eat human flesh." In 1550, Peter Martyr D'Anghiera included the following in book five of his De Orbe Novo upon relating to the reader the news of Columbus's discovery: "Every creature in this sublunary world that gives birth to something, either immediately afterwards closes its womb or rests for a period. The new world, however, seems not to be governed by such a rule, for each day it creates without ceasing and brings forth new things, which continue to furnish, sprites and daemons gifted with power, many of whom are female. These she-warriors took over Columbus's vessel on one occasion. They were half-naked and danced for the sailors inviting them to drink and seducing them. Once the sailors were drunk, the warrior women took them to be eaten. The admiral escaped by chance, having chained himself to the mast." Martyr had read The Odyssey. But now, in the library of the island of Alexandria, also known as the Faro or The Garden, free women and men read also The Penelopiad. In the 1603 English translation of Michel de Montaigne's Essay on Cannibals, made by Giovanni Floro, the following passage reads: "These creatures of air, the Cannibals, retain alive and vigorous their genuine, their most useful and natural, virtues and properties." Montaigne goes on to speak of their abilities to control air and water, to build temples in sky-high mountains, and to summon the old ones from the depths of the sea in order to raise an Universal Army whose aim is to storm the heavens. William Shakespeare, a personal friend of Giovanni Floro, owned and annotated a copy of Montaigne's essay. In his copy there is a handwritten instruction to present the creature of air, now enslaved and imprisoned in the bowels of the earth, as an animal, or a girl. In The Tempest, Shakespeare has the magus Prospero issue this warning to his daughter Miranda: "We cannot miss her. She makes our fire, fetch in our wood, and serves in offices that profits us." He called that spirit Caliban and observed that a man or a woman could represent the character. The name was an alliteration of Cannibal. The island in which the action takes place originally belonged to Caliban, who inherited it from a powerful woman who practiced theurgy. Prospero stole it using his magic to shackle Caliban. Caliban curses Prospero's goety with these words: "You taught me your language, and my profit on't is, I know how to curse. The red plague rid you, for learning me your language." Later on Miranda joined Caliban. In 1878, Ernst Renan made Caliban the incarnation of the people who were taking to the streets ready to bring about the assault on the heavens. It is said these rebels closed the gates of heaven and instead opened an immense library in an island called The Fountain. Years later, surrealist writers Simone and Pierre Yoyotte wrote of tranquil atmospheres and dance as well as the delirious Theory of the Fountain. "The fountain constitutes a sexual provocation of a very simple type, when the water or the liquid that this fountain procures flows brusquely in small quantities ... On the other hand, the fountain is the mouth: the fountain following like the body of an automobile in the hollow of the hand." The fountain is an island, it is sex, a mouth and a hand. Also a beverage, of limpid metallic taste or a silver elixir provoked by an alchemists' or a witch's boiling. Those who drink the elixir are said to acquire the vision of the Nohor. Around the same time Aimé Cesaire pointed out that Ariel was like the air, incapable of definition, a mulatto always ready to negotiate and consent in servitude to save his own skin. In contrast, he said, Caliban is a Nohor. A free black slave both male and female. And she's an incarnation of both Shango and Osun, a warrior woman, a black goddess-devil. Now, Caliban commands the Universal Army that fights against dipenda or slavery, for uhuru or freedom, which is sexual provocation and water, the mouth and the hollow of the hand, ripe fruit and mirrors of obsidian. Uhuru, the mouth, says: Here. I'm here. Dipenda darkens the sun, like a swarm of locusts and ruins the country. Uhuru is a woman, and she is intransigent. She was called little girl, first, and then Fatima in Haiti. She was also the madness of Christophe and Patrice Lumumba. She is a woman, and she is an idea. Invincible like the hope of the people, like a travelling bushfire, like the pollen moving from wind to wind. She is no longer a girl, no longer little. She is the field of the civil war. She is with the fish people. When they found the bottle, she helped them to free the djinn and fly away together into the fire. The fire this time. She will not be in the mountain listening to the sermon. She will be the mountain. She will be in the ravine. No longer little, no longer a girl. But a semi-sorcerer. She is endowed with the vision of a Nohor. Her inner world closely mingled with images and projections. So much so, as Heriberto Cogollo wrote in 1973, that "it is sometimes difficult to make the distinction between what I see and what is actually my own. What I do know is that I would like to be able to also show the inner world I gaze upon." She is a tree,

a she-warrior armed with seven thousand volumes. A Nohor.
And a hodoo hollerin' bebop ghost. This is her song. It tells
the adventures of those who defied time and went on to build
a Pharos illuminating the world from Alexandria. The place
they call The Fountain. You Lady Day.

You
hodoo
hollerin'
bebop
ghost.

TO BE CONTINUED

Image citations